Preface

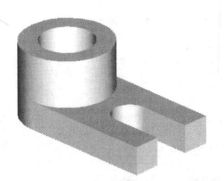

The primary goal of *AutoCAD® 2002 Tutorial: 2D Fundamentals* is to introduce the aspects of **Computer Aided Design and Drafting (CADD)**. This text is intended to be used as a training guide for students and professionals. This text covers *AutoCAD® 2002* and the lessons proceed in a pedagogical fashion to guide you from constructing basic shapes to making multiview drawings. This text takes a hands-on, exercise-intensive approach to all the important CAD techniques and concepts. This textbook contains a series of ten tutorial style lessons designed to introduce beginning CAD users to **AutoCAD® 2002**. This text is also helpful to AutoCAD users upgrading from a previous release of the software. The new improvements and key enhancements of the software are incorporated into the lessons. You will learn to use the new AutoCAD Heads-up Design™ interface, which enables you to focus on the design, not on the keyboard. Other features, such as the AutoCAD® 2002 AutoTrack™ feature, the WYSIWYG (What You See Is What You Get) plotting feature, the Named Plot Style feature, and Layout plotting are also introduced in the lessons. The CAD techniques and concepts discussed in this text are also designed to serve as the foundation to the more advanced parametric feature-based CAD packages such as AutoCAD® Mechanical Desktop and AutoCAD® Inventor. The basic premise of this book is that the more designs you create using AutoCAD® 2002, the better you learn the software. With this in mind, each lesson introduces a new set of commands and concepts, building on previous lessons. This book does not attempt to cover all of AutoCAD® 2002's features, only to provide an introduction to the software. It is intended to help you establish a good basis for exploring and growing in the exciting field of Computer Aided Engineering.

Acknowledgments

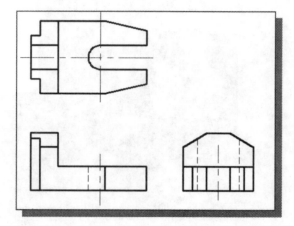

This book would not have been possible without a great deal of support. First, special thanks to two great teachers, Prof. George R. Schade of University of Nebraska-Lincoln and Mr. Denwu Lee, who taught me the fundamentals, the intrigue, and the sheer fun of Computer Aided Engineering.

My deep appreciation goes to Prof. Jack Zecher, Indiana University Purdue University Indianapolis, for the production of the multimedia CD, the audio-visual format of this text.

The effort and support of the editorial and production staff of Schroff Development Corporation is gratefully acknowledged. I would especially like to thank Stephen Schroff and Mary Schmidt for their support and helpful suggestions during this project.

I am grateful that the Mechanical Engineering Technology Department of Oregon Institute of Technology has provided me with an excellent environment in which to pursue my interests in teaching and research. I would especially like to thank Professor Brian Moravec and Emeritus Professor Charles Hermach for helpful comments and encouragement.

Finally, truly unbounded thanks are due to my wife Hsiu-Ling and our daughter Casandra for their understanding and encouragement throughout this project.

Randy H. Shih
Klamath Falls, Oregon

Table of Contents

Lesson 3
Construction and Editing Tools

Lesson 4
Object Properties and Organization

Lesson 5
Orthographic Views in Multiview Drawings

Lesson 6
Basic Dimensioning and Notes

Lesson 7
Templates and Plotting

Lesson 8
Auxiliary Views and Editing with GRIPS

Lesson 9
Section Views

Lesson 10
Assembly Drawings and Blocks

Lesson 1
Getting Started

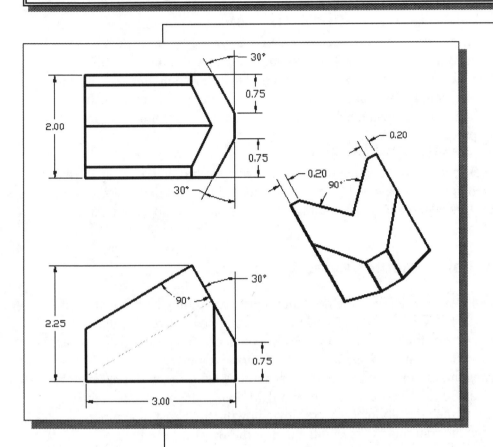

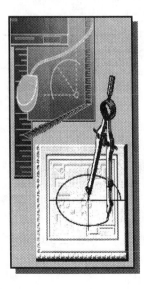

Learning Objectives

♦ **Development of Computer Aided Design**
♦ **Why use AutoCAD 2002**
♦ **Getting started with AutoCAD 2002**
♦ **The AutoCAD Today dialog box and Units Setup**
♦ **AutoCAD 2002 Screen Layout**
♦ **Mouse Buttons**

Introduction

Computer Aided Design (CAD) is the process of doing designs with the aid of computers. This includes the generation of computer models, analysis of design data, and the creation of the necessary drawings. **AutoCAD® 2002** is a computer aided design software developed by *Autodesk Inc*. The **AutoCAD® 2002** software is a tool that can be used for design and drafting activities. The two-dimensional and three-dimensional models created in **AutoCAD® 2002** can be transferred to other computer programs for further analysis and testing. The computer models can also be used in manufacturing equipment such as machining centers, lathes, mills, or rapid prototyping machines to manufacture the product.

The rapid changes in the field of computer aided design have brought exciting advances in industry. Recent advances have made the long-sought goal of reducing design time, producing prototypes faster, and achieving higher product quality closer to a reality.

Development of Computer Aided Design

Computer Aided Design is a relatively new and rapidly expanding area. The transistor was invented in 1948, and soon after general purpose computers were invented in the 1950s and 1960s. One of the most important developments in computer graphics was the publication of Ivan Sutherland's *Sketchpad* (MIT doctoral dissertation) in 1963. This is considered the beginning of interactive computer graphics. During that time, several companies, such as General Motors, Boeing, and IBM, began development of interactive CAD programs, but such developments were slowed by the high cost of computer hardware, the high programming cost, and the non-portability of the software.

The 1970s were marked by significant progress in the development of microprocessors. It was in 1971 that Ted Hoff developed the first microprocessor. The era of the personal computer (PC) had begun through the development of Large-Scale Integrated Circuits (LSIC) in which all circuitry of the central processing unit (CPU) is on one chip. In the 1980s, improvements in computer hardware brought the power of mainframes to the desktop.

Computer modeling technology has advanced along with the computer hardware. The CAD programs evolved into design tools rather than just drafting tools. During these years of development, modeling schemes progressed from two-dimensional (2D) wireframe to three-dimensional (3D) wireframe, to surface modeling and, finally, to solid modeling.

Wireframes are models consisting of locations of points and lines between appropriate pairs of points. The lines are used to represent transitions; such as from surface to surface. Lines are also a very economical way of representing geometry.

The development of the 3D wireframe modeler was a major leap in the area of computer modeling. The computer database in the 3D wireframe modeler contains the locations of all the points in space coordinates and it is sufficient to create just one model rather than multiple models. This single 3D model can then be viewed from any direction as needed. The 3D wireframe modelers require the least computer power and achieve reasonably good representation of 3D models. But because surface definition is not part of a wireframe model, all wireframe images have the inherent problem of ambiguity.

Surface modeling is the logical development in computer geometry modeling to follow the 3D wireframe modeling scheme by organizing and grouping of the edges that define polygonal surfaces. Surface modeling describes the part surfaces but not the interiors. Designers are still required to interactively examine surface models to insure that the various surfaces on a model are contiguous throughout. Many of the concepts used in 3D wireframe and surface modelers are incorporated in the solid modeling scheme, but it is solid modeling that offers the most advantages as a design tool.

In the solid modeling presentation scheme, the solid definitions include nodes, edges, and surfaces, and it is a complete and unambiguous mathematical representation of a precisely enclosed and filled volume. Unlike the surface modeling method, solid modelers start with a solid or use topology rules to guarantee that all of the surfaces are stitched together properly.

In this text, we will follow a logical order, parallel to the development of computer geometric modeling, in learning the fundamental concepts and commands of **AutoCAD**® **2002**. We will begin with basic geometric constructions, orthographic projections, and then move toward the more advanced features of **AutoCAD**® **2002**. We will also discuss and demonstrate the general procedure required in creating three-dimensional solid models. The techniques presented in this text will also serve as the foundation to enter the world of advanced three-dimensional solid modeling using packages such as **AutoCAD Mechanical Desktop** and **AutoCAD Architectural Desktop**.

Why use AutoCAD® 2002?

AutoCAD® was first introduced to the public in late 1982, and was one of the first CAD software products available for personal computers. Since 1984, **AutoCAD**® has established a reputation for being the most widely used PC-based CAD software around the world. By 2001, it was estimated that there were over 3.5 million **AutoCAD**® users in more than 150 countries worldwide. **AutoCAD**® **2002** is the seventeenth release, with many added features and enhancements, of the original **AutoCAD**® software produced by *Autodesk Inc.*

CAD provides us with a wide range of benefits; in most cases, the result of using CAD is increased accuracy and productivity. First of all, the computer offers much higher accuracy than the traditional method of drafting and design. Traditionally, drafting and detailing are the most expensive cost element in a project and the biggest bottleneck.

With CAD systems, such as **AutoCAD® 2002**, the tedious drafting and detailing tasks are simplified through the use of many of the CAD geometric construction tools, such as *grids*, *snap*, *trim*, and *auto-dimensioning*. Dimensions and notes are always legible in CAD drawings and, in most cases, CAD systems can produce higher quality prints compared to traditional hand drawings.

CAD also offers much-needed flexibility in design and drafting. A CAD model generated on a computer consists of numeric data that describe the geometry of the object. This allows the designers and clients to see something tangible and to interpret the ramifications of the design. In many cases, it is also possible to simulate operating conditions on the computer and observe the results. Any kind of geometric shape stored in the database can be easily duplicated. For large and complex designs and drawings, particularly those involving similar shapes and repetitive operations, CAD approaches are very efficient and effective. Because computer designs and models can be altered easily, a multitude of design options can be examined and presented to a client before any construction or manufacturing actually takes place. Making changes to a CAD database is generally much faster than making changes to a traditional hand drawing. Only the affected components of the design need to be modified and the drawings can be plotted again. In addition, the greatest benefit is that, once the CAD model is created, it can be used over and over again. The CAD models can also be transferred into manufacturing equipment such as machining centers, lathes, mills, or rapid prototyping machines to manufacture the product directly.

CAD, however, does not replace every design activity. CAD may help, but it does not replace the designer's experience with geometry, graphical conventions and standards for the specific field. CAD is a powerful tool, but the use of this tool does not guarantee correct results; the designer is still responsible for using good design practice and applying good judgement. CAD will supplement these skills to ensure that the best design is obtained.

CAD designs and drawings are stored in binary form, usually as CAD files, to magnetic devices such as diskettes and hard disks. The information stored in CAD files usually requires much less physical space in comparison to traditional hand drawings. However, the information stored inside the computer is not indestructible. On the contrary, the electronic format of information is very fragile and sensitive to the environment. Heat or cold can damage the information stored on magnetic storage devices. A power failure while you are creating a design could wipe out the many hours you spent working in front of your computer monitor. It is a good habit to save your work periodically, just in case something might and probably will go wrong while you are working on your design. In general, you should save your work onto the disk at an interval of every 15 to 20 minutes. You should also save your work before you make any major modifications to the design. It is also a good habit to periodically make backup copies of your work and put them in a safe place.

This textbook contains a series of ten tutorial style lessons designed to introduce students to **AutoCAD® 2002**. The new improvements and key enhancements of the software are incorporated into the lessons. You will learn to use the new **AutoCAD Heads-up**

Design™ interface, which enables you to focus on the design, not on the keyboard. The major enhancement of **AutoCAD**® **2002** is the introduction of the *Internet-Driven Design* approach, where we can access drawing files, symbol libraries, an intranet-based AutoCAD bulletin board, and the Autodesk Point A design portal within **AutoCAD**® **2002**. We can also receive live product updates over the internet, upload projects to a web-based storage location, read industry news, and access productivity tools. We can use a wizard to publish web pages that include drawing images. We will also cover the new *Visual, Intuitive Learning and Assistance* that are user-friendly and helpful to new users. The new AutoCAD AutoTrack™ feature, the onscreen lineweight feature, the WYSIWYG (What You See Is What You Get) plotting feature, the Named Plot Style feature and Layout plotting feature are also introduced in the lessons.

Now that you are ready to move on, let us begin the learning experience with **AutoCAD**® **2002,** which you will find interesting and fun. And welcome to the exciting world of **Computer Aided Design**.

Getting started with AutoCAD® 2002

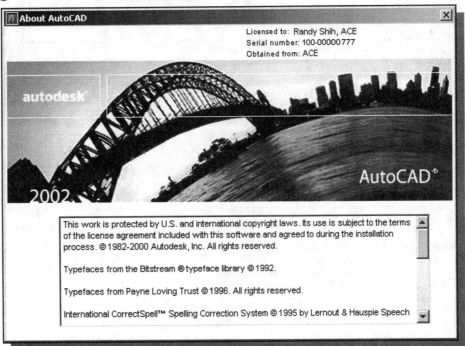

How to start **AutoCAD**® **2002** depends on the type of workstation and the particular software configuration you are using. With most *Windows* systems, you may select the **AutoCAD 2002** option on the *Start* menu or select the **AutoCAD 2002** icon on the *Desktop*. Consult with your instructor or technical support personnel if you have difficulty starting the software.

The program takes a while to load, so be patient. Eventually the **AutoCAD**® **2002** *drawing screen* and the *AutoCAD Today startup dialog box* will appear on the screen.

The tutorials in this text are based on the assumption that you are using **AutoCAD®** **2002**'s default settings. If your system has been customized for other uses, some of the settings may not work with the step-by-step instructions in the tutorials. Contact your instructor and/or technical support personnel to restore the default software configuration.

The AutoCAD 2002 Today dialog box and Units Setup

Once the program is loaded into the memory, the **AutoCAD® 2002** startup dialog box, *AutoCAD 2002 Today*, appears at the center of the screen.

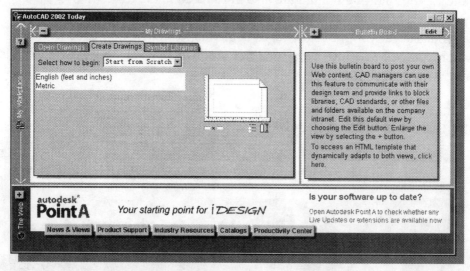

◆ The *AutoCAD Today* startup dialog box is divided into two sections: *My Workplace* and *The Web*. Using these options, we can communicate our designs to other members of the design team and/or customers around the world.

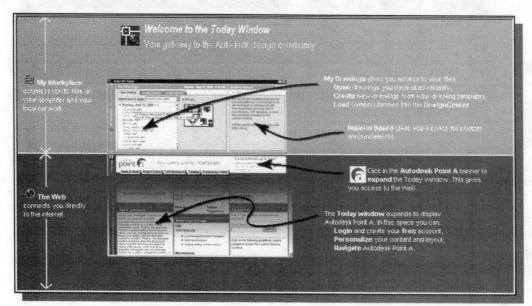

In the *My Workplace* section of the *AutoCAD Today* dialogue box, the following three options are available as startup options: **Open Drawings, Create Drawings,** and **Symbol Libraries.** We can *open existing files, create new drawings* or access the AutoCAD *symbol libraries* options.

- Select the **Create Drawings** tab with a single click of the left-mouse-button in the *My Workplace* section of the *AutoCAD Today* dialogue box.

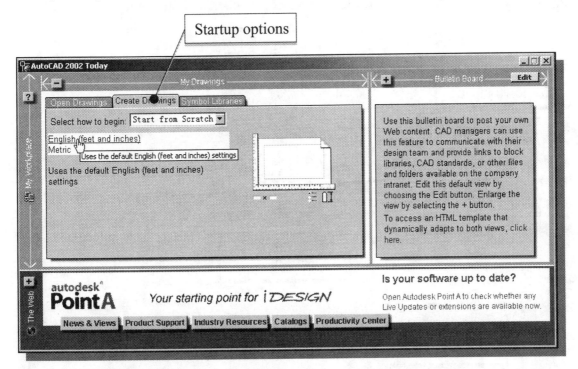

Under the **Create Drawings** tab, three options are available: *Start from Scratch, Use a Template,* and *Use a Wizard*. The default *Start from Scratch* option allows us to start a new CAD file without setting any preferences. We will explain and demonstrate the use of the other options in the following lessons.

Below the *Startup* option icons is the *Default Settings* section, which lets us specify the units to be used with the CAD file. When starting a new CAD file, the first thing we should do is choose the units we would like to use. We will use the default **English (feet and Inches)** setting for this example.

- Move the cursor on top of the **English (feet and inches)** option and notice a brief explanation of the option is displayed as shown in the figure above.

- Use the left-mouse-button to select the **English (feet and Inches)** units as the units to be used for the design.

AutoCAD® 2002 Screen Layout

The default **AutoCAD® 2002** *drawing screen* contains the *pull-down* menus, the *Standard* toolbar, the *Object Properties* toolbar, the *Draw* toolbar, the *Modify* toolbar, the *command prompt area*, the *Status Bar* and the *AutoCAD Active Assistance*. A line of quick help text appears at the bottom of the window as you move the *mouse cursor* over different icons. You may resize the **AutoCAD® 2002** drawing window by click and drag at the edges of the window, or relocate the window by click and drag at the window title area.

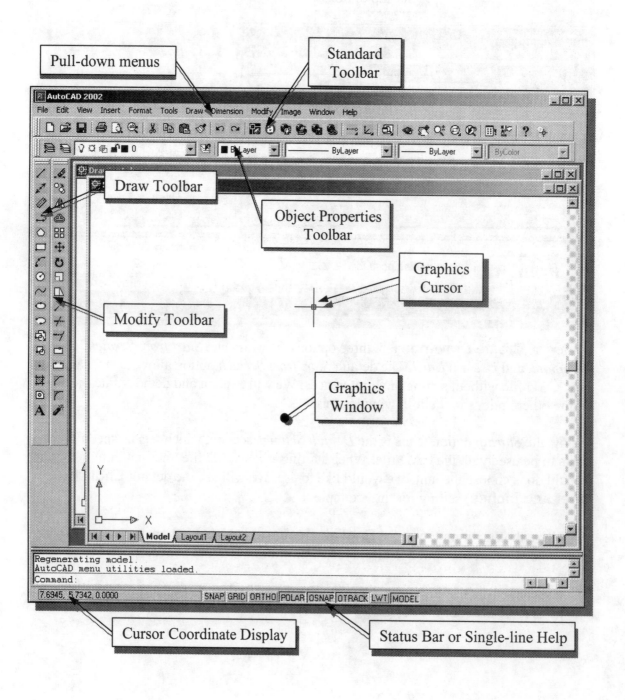

- **Pull-down Menus**

The *pull-down* menus at the top of the main window contain operations that you can use for all modes of the system.

- **Standard Toolbar**

The *Standard* toolbar at the top of the AutoCAD window allows us quick access to frequently used commands. We can customize the toolbar by adding and removing sets of options or individual commands.

- **Object Properties Toolbar**

The *Object Properties* toolbar contains tools to help manipulate the graphical object properties, such as color, line type, and layer.

- **Graphics Window**

The *graphics window* is the area where models and drawings are displayed.

- **Graphics Cursor or Crosshairs**

The *graphics cursor*, or *crosshairs*, shows the location of the pointing device in the graphics window. The coordinates of the cursor are displayed at the bottom of the screen layout. The cursor's appearance depends on the selected command or option.

- **Command Prompt Area**

The bottom section of the screen layout provides status information for an operation and it is also the area for data input.

- **Draw Toolbar and Modify Toolbar**

Additional toolbars are available in **AutoCAD® 2002**, and contain groups of buttons that allow us to pick commands quickly, without searching through a menu structure. The *Draw* toolbar and *Modify* toolbar contain icons for basic draw and modify commands.

Mouse Buttons

AutoCAD® 2002 utilizes the mouse buttons extensively. In learning AutoCAD® 2002's interactive environment, it is important to understand the basic functions of the mouse buttons. It is highly recommended that you use a mouse or a tablet with AutoCAD® 2002 since the package uses the buttons for various functions.

- **Left mouse button**

The **left-mouse-button** is used for most operations, such as selecting menus and icons, or picking graphic entities. One click of the button is used to select icons, menus and form entries, and to pick graphic items.

- **Right mouse button**

The **right-mouse-button** is used to bring up additional available options. The software also utilizes the **right-mouse-button** as the same as the **ENTER** key, and is often used to accept the default setting to a prompt or to end a process.

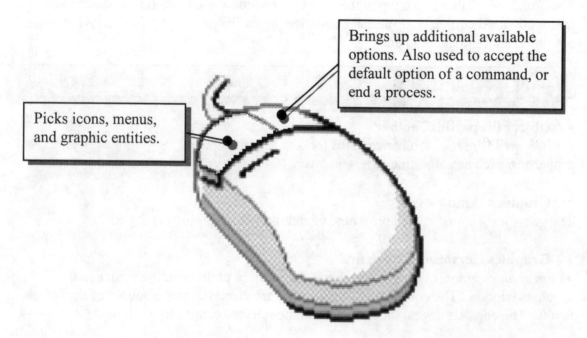

Brings up additional available options. Also used to accept the default option of a command, or end a process.

Picks icons, menus, and graphic entities.

[Esc] - Canceling commands

The [**Esc**] key is used to cancel a command in AutoCAD® 2002. The [**Esc**] key is located near the top-left corner of the keyboard. Sometimes, it may be necessary to press the [**Esc**] key twice to cancel a command; it depends on where we are in the command sequence. For some commands, the [**Esc**] key is used to exit the command.

On-Line Help

❖ Several types of on-line help are available at any time during an **AutoCAD®2002** session. The **AutoCAD®2002** software provides many on-line help options:

- **Active Assistance**:

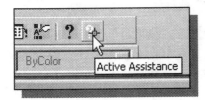

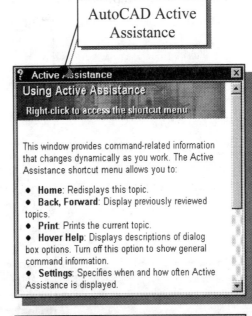

AutoCAD Active Assistance

The *Active Assistance* option provides an instant help that dynamically displays information on the activated command. The guidance from the *Active Assistance* system enables users to quickly get started on performing desired tasks. In the *Active Assistance* window, links to additional information are also available. Clicking a blue-text-link expands the current *Active Assistance* topic.

- To turn *off* the *Active Assistance*, right-click the **Active Assistance** icon located in the system tray and choose **Exit**.

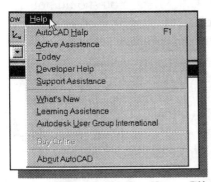

- **Pull-down menu**: Click on the **HELP** option in the pull-down menu to access the **AutoCAD®2002 Help menu system**. Notice the different help options available in the pull-down list.

- **Standard Toolbar**: Click on the [**?**] icon in the *Standard* toolbar to access Autodesk On-line Help: User Documentation. Note the **Active Assistance** icon is located right next to the **Help** icon.

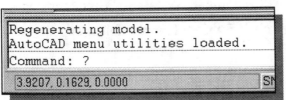

- **Command line and function key [F1]**: Press the [**F1**] key or enter a question mark [**?**] at the command prompt to access the **AutoCAD On-line Help system**.

Leaving AutoCAD® 2002

To leave **AutoCAD® 2002**, use the left-mouse-button and click on **File** at the top of the **AutoCAD® 2002** screen window, then choose **Exit** from the pull-down menu or type *QUIT* in the command prompt area.

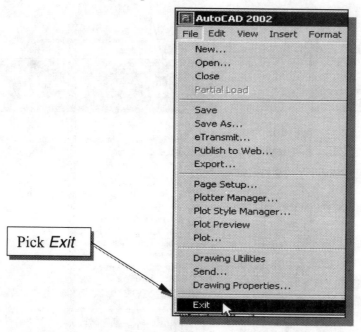

Pick *Exit*

Creating a CAD file folder

It is a good practice to create a separate folder to store your CAD files. You should not save your CAD files in the same folder where the **AutoCAD® 2002** application is located. It is much easier to organize and backup your project files if they are in a separate folder. Making folders within this folder for different types of projects will help you organize your CAD files even further. When creating CAD files in **AutoCAD® 2002**, it is strongly recommended that you *save* your CAD files on the hard drive. However, if you do want to save your files on a floppy drive, be sure to exit the **AutoCAD® 2002** program before removing the diskette from the drive. The better alternative is to save the files on the hard drive and then copy the files onto a floppy diskette under the operating system.

To create a new folder:
1. In *My Computer*, or start the **Windows Explorer** under the *Start* menu, open the folder in which you want to create a new folder.

2. On the **File** menu, point to **New**, and then click **Folder**. The new folder appears with a temporary name.

3. Type a name for the new folder, and then press **ENTER**.

Lesson 2
Geometric Construction Basics

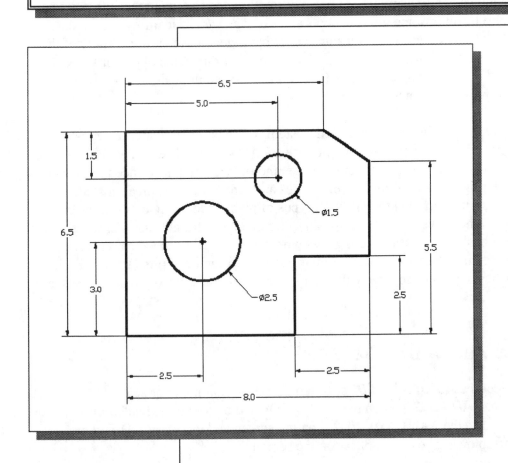

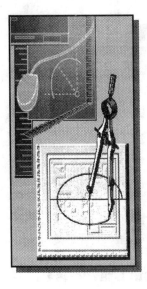

Learning Objectives

- ♦ **Create and Save AutoCAD drawing files.**
- ♦ **Use the AutoCAD visual reference commands.**
- ♦ **Draw, using the LINE and CIRCLE commands.**
- ♦ **Use the ERASE command.**
- ♦ **Define Positions using the Basic Entry methods.**
- ♦ **Use the AutoCAD Pan Realtime option.**

Introduction

Learning to use a CAD system is similar to learning a new language. We need to begin with the basic alphabet and learn how to use it correctly and effectively through practice. This will require learning some new concepts and skills as well as learning a different vocabulary. All CAD systems create designs using basic geometric entities. Many of the constructions used in technical designs are based upon two-dimensional planar geometry. The method and number of operations that are required to accomplish the constructions are different from one system to another.

In order to become effective in using a CAD system, we must learn to create geometric entities quickly and accurately. In learning to use a CAD system, **lines** and **circles** are the first two, and perhaps the most important two, geometric entities that we need to master the skills of creating and modifying. Straight lines and circles are used in almost all technical designs. In examining the different types of planar geometric entities, we can see that triangles and polygons are planar figures bounded by straight lines. Ellipses and Splines can be constructed by connecting arcs with different radii. As we gain some experience in creating lines and circles, similar procedures can be applied to create other geometric entities. In this lesson, we will examine the different ways of creating lines and circles in **AutoCAD® 2002**.

Starting Up AutoCAD® 2002

1. Select the **AutoCAD 2002** option on the *Program* menu or select the **AutoCAD 2002** icon on the *Desktop*. Once the program is loaded into memory, the **AutoCAD® 2002** drawing screen and the *AutoCAD Today* startup dialog box will appear on the screen.

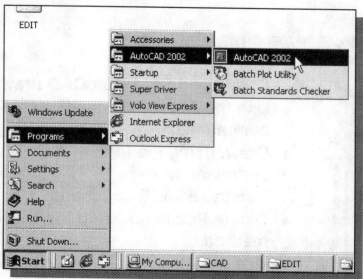

2. In the *AutoCAD Today* startup dialog box, select the **Create Drawings** tab with a single click of the left-mouse-button.

3. Confirm the startup option is set to **Start from Scratch**, as shown in the figure below.

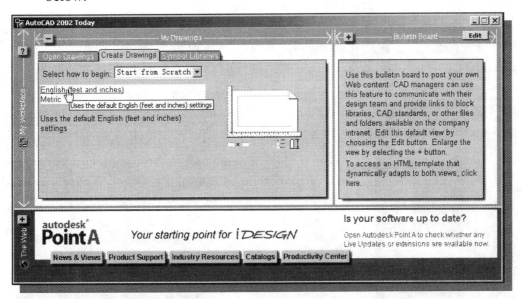

4. In the *Default Settings* section, pick **English (feet and Inches)** as the drawing units.

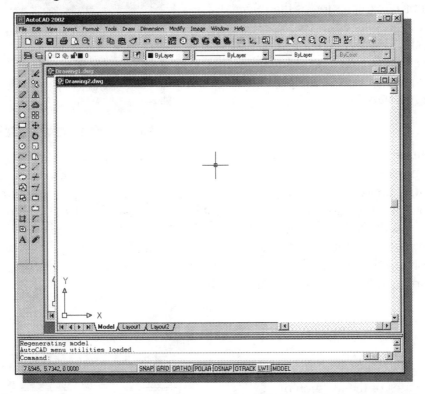

➤ Note that two graphics windows, *Drawing1* and *Drawing2*, are opened. AutoCAD automatically assigns generic names, *Drawing X*, as new drawings are created. In our example, AutoCAD opened the first graphics window (*Drawing1*), using the default system units. The second graphics window (*Drawing2*) was opened when we chose to create a new drawing from scratch using the default English units.

Using the *Line* command

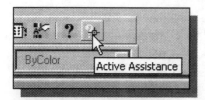

1. Click on the **Active Assistance** icon to activate the option.

2. Move the graphics cursor to the first icon in the *Draw* toolbar. This icon is the **Line** icon. A *help-tip* box appears next to the cursor and a brief description of the icon is displayed at the bottom of the AutoCAD drawing screen: "*Creates Straight line segments: LINE.*"

3. Select the icon by clicking once with the left-mouse-button; this will activate the *Line* command.

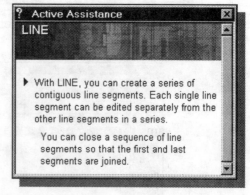

➢ Notice a brief explanation of the selected command is displayed in the *Active Assistance* window. It is highly recommended that you read the explanations to gain some insights on the basic assumptions and general procedure of using AutoCAD.

4. In the command prompt area, near the bottom of the AutoCAD drawing screen, the message "*_line Specify first point:*" is displayed. AutoCAD expects us to identify the starting location of a straight line. Move the graphics cursor inside the graphics window and watch the display of the coordinates of the graphics cursor at the bottom of the AutoCAD drawing screen. The three numbers represent the location of the cursor in the X, Y, and Z directions. We can treat the graphics window as if it was a piece of paper and we are using the graphics cursor as if it were a pencil with which to draw.

Coordinates of the location of the graphics cursor.

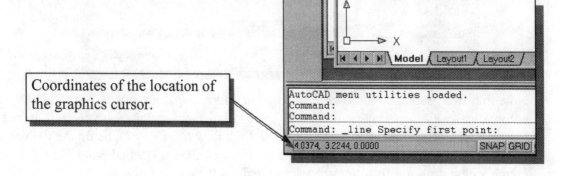

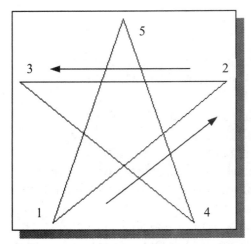

5. We will create a freehand sketch of a five-point star using the *Line* command. We will create the sketch near the center of the drawing window. Do not be overly concerned with the actual size or the accuracy of your freehand sketch. This exercise is to give you a feel for the **AutoCAD® 2002** user interface.

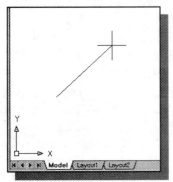

6. We will start at a location about one-third from the bottom of the graphics window. Left-click once to position the starting point of our first line. This will be *point 1* of our sketch. Next move the cursor upward and toward the right side of *point 1*. Notice the rubber-band line that follows the graphics cursor in the graphics window. Left-click again (*point 2*) and we have created the first line of our sketch.

7. Move the cursor to the left of *point 2* and create a horizontal line about the same length as the first line on the screen.

8. Repeat the above steps and complete the freehand sketch by adding three more lines (from *point 3* to *point 4*, *point 4* to *point 5*, and then connect to *point 5* back to *point 1*).

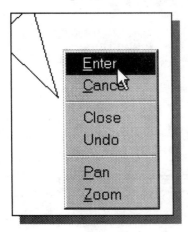

9. Notice that the *Line* command remains activated even after we connected the last segment of the line to the starting point *(point 1)* of our sketch. Inside the graphics window, **click once with the right-mouse-button** and a popup menu appears on the screen.

10. Select **Enter** with the left-mouse-button to end the *Line* command. (This is equivalent to hitting the [**ENTER**] key on the keyboard. Note that the right-mouse-click brings up the option menu which provides more options and we should become used to using it.)

11. On your own, move the cursor near *point 2* and *point 3*, and estimate the length of the horizontal line by watching the displayed coordinates for each point at the bottom of the screen.

Visual reference

The method we just used to create the freehand sketch is known as the **interactive method**, where we use the cursor to specify locations on the screen. This method is perhaps the fastest way to specify locations on the screen. However, it is rather difficult to try to create a line of a specific length by watching the displayed coordinates. It would be helpful to know what one-inch or one-meter looks like on the screen while we are creating entities. **AutoCAD® 2002** provides us with many tools to aid the construction of our designs. We will use the **Grid** and **Snap** options to get a visual reference as to the size of objects and learn to restrict the movement of the cursor to a set increment on the screen.

The *Status Bar* area is located at the bottom of the AutoCAD drawing screen. The words *SNAP*, *GRID*, *ORTHO*, *POLAR*, *OSNAP*, *OSNAP*, *OTRACK*, *LWT* and *MODEL* appearing to the right of the coordinates are buttons that we can left-click to turn these special options *ON* and *OFF*. When the corresponding button is *highlighted*, the specific option is turned *ON*. These buttons act as toggle switches; each click of the button will toggle the option *ON* or *OFF*. Using the buttons is a quick and easy way to make changes to these *drawing aid* options. We can toggle the options on and off in the middle of another command.

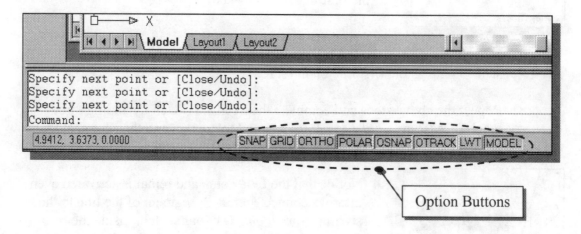

Option Buttons

GRID ON

1. Left-click the **GRID** button in the *Status Bar* to turn **ON** the *GRID* option. (Notice in the command prompt area, the message *"<Grid on>"* is also displayed.)

```
Specify next point or [Close/Undo]:
Specify next point or [Close/Undo]:
Command:  <Grid on>
Command:
4.9412, 3.6373, 0.0000        SNAP GRID ORTHO POLAR
```

2. Move the cursor inside the graphics window, and estimate the distance in between the grid points by watching the coordinates display at the bottom of the screen.

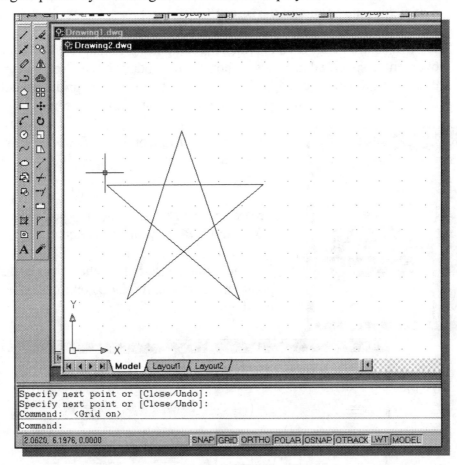

> The *GRID* option creates a pattern of dots that extends over an area on the screen. Using the grid is similar to placing a sheet of grid paper under a drawing. The grid helps you align objects and visualize the distance between them. The grid is not displayed in the plotted drawing. The default grid spacing, which means the distance in between two dots on the screen, is 0.5 inches. We can see that the sketched horizontal line in the above sketch is about 3.5 inches long.

SNAP ON

1. Left-click the *SNAP* button in the *Status Bar* to turn *ON* the *SNAP* option.

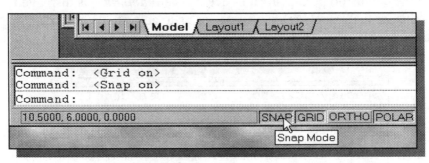

2. Move the cursor inside the graphics window, and move the cursor diagonally on the screen. Observe the movement of the cursor and watch the *coordinates display* at the bottom of the screen.

➢ The *SNAP* option controls an invisible rectangular grid that restricts cursor movement to specified intervals. When *SNAP* mode is on, the screen cursor and all input coordinates are snapped to the nearest point on the grid. The default snap interval is 0.5 inches, and aligned to the grid points on the screen.

3. Click on the **Line** icon in the *Draw* toolbar. In the command prompt area, the message "*_line Specify first point:*" is displayed.

4. Create another sketch of the five-point star with the *GRID* and *SNAP* options switched on.

5. Use the right-mouse-button and select **Enter** in the popup menu to end the *Line* command if you have not done so.

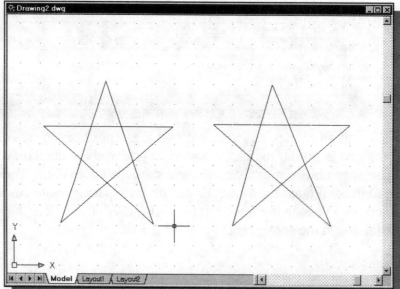

6. In the command prompt area, notice that "***Command:***" is displayed. This indicates that AutoCAD is waiting for us to activate the next desired command.

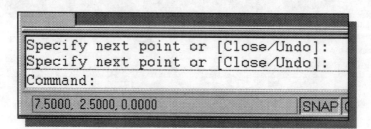

Using the *ERASER*

❖ One of the advantages of using a CAD system is the ability to remove entities without leaving any marks. We will erase two of the lines using the *Erase* command.

1. Pick **Erase** in the *Modify* toolbar. (The icon is the first icon in the *Modify* toolbar. The icon is a picture of an eraser at the end of a pencil.) The message *"Select objects"* is displayed in the command prompt area and AutoCAD awaits us to select the objects to erase.

2. Left-click the *SNAP* button on the *Status Bar* to turn off the *SNAP* option so that we can more easily move the cursor on top of objects. We can toggle the *Status Bar* options *ON* or *OFF* in the middle of another command.

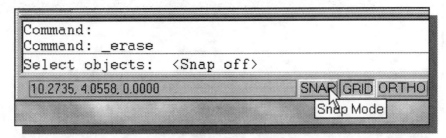

3. Select any two lines on the screen, and right-mouse-click once to accept the selections. The selected two lines are erased.

Repeat the last command

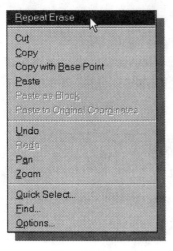

1. Inside the *graphics window*, click once with the **right-mouse-button** to bring up the popup option menu.

2. Pick **Repeat Erase**, with the left-mouse-button, in the popup menu to repeat the last command. Notice the other options available in the popup menu.

➢ **AutoCAD® 2002** offers many options to accomplish the same task. Throughout this text, we will emphasize the use of the **AutoCAD Heads-up Design**™ interface, which means we focus on the screen, not on the keyboard.

3. Move the cursor to a location that is above and toward the left side of the entities on the screen. Left-mouse-click once to start a corner of a rubber-band window.

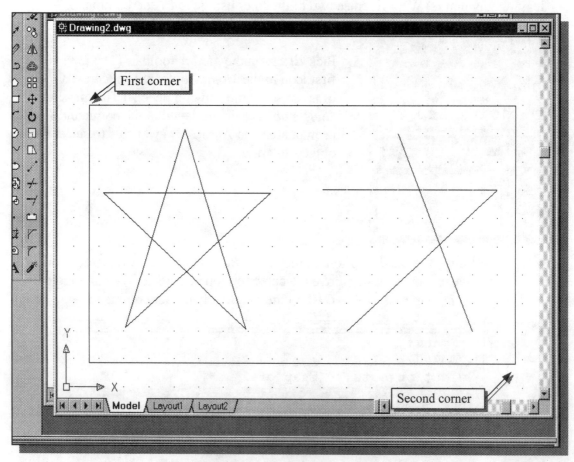

4. Move the cursor toward the right and below the entities, and then left-mouse-click to enclose all the entities inside the **selection window**. Notice all entities that are inside the window are selected.

5. Inside the graphics window, **right-mouse-click** to proceed with erasing the selected entities.

> On your own, create a sketch of your choice using the **Line** command. Experiment with using the different commands we have discussed so far, such as switching the *GRID* and *SNAP* options on and off in the middle of a command.

❖ Do not be in a hurry to rush through the tutorials. Build up your CAD skills by familiarizing yourself with the commands and options demonstrated, along with the concepts discussed in the lessons. Feel free to repeat, at any time, any portions of the lessons.

The CAD Database and the User Coordinate System

❖ Designs and drawings created in a CAD system are usually defined and stored using sets of points in what is called **world space**. In most CAD systems, the world space is defined using a three-dimensional *Cartesian coordinate system*. Three mutually perpendicular axes, usually referred to as the X, Y, and Z axes, define this system. The intersection of the three coordinate axes forms a point called the **origin**. Any point in world space can then be defined as the distance from the origin in the X, Y and Z directions. In most CAD systems, the directions of the arrows shown on the axes identify the positive sides of the coordinates.

A CAD file, which is the electronic version of the design, contains data that describe the entities created in the CAD system. Information such as the coordinate values in world space for all endpoints, center points, etc., along with the descriptions of the types of entities are all stored in the file. Knowing that AutoCAD stores designs by keeping coordinate data helps us understand the inputs required to create entities.

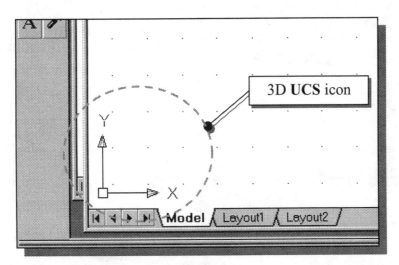

The icon near the bottom left corner of the default AutoCAD graphics window shows the positive X-direction and positive Y-direction of the coordinate system that is active. In AutoCAD, the coordinate system that is used to create entities is called the **User Coordinate System** (UCS). By default, the **User Coordinate System** is aligned to the world coordinate system (**WCS**). The **world coordinate system** is a coordinate system used by AutoCAD as the basis for defining all objects and other coordinate systems defined by the users. We can think of the **origin** of the **world coordinate system** as a fixed point being used as a reference for all measurements. The default orientation of the Z-axis can be considered as positive values in front of the monitor and negative values inside the monitor.

Changing to the 2D UCS icon Display

❖ In **AutoCAD® 2002**, the *UCS* icon is displayed in various ways to help us visualize the orientation of the drawing plane.

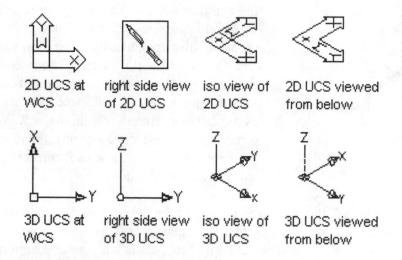

2D UCS at   right side view   iso view of   2D UCS viewed
WCS   of 2D UCS   2D UCS   from below

3D UCS at   right side view   iso view of   3D UCS viewed
WCS   of 3D UCS   3D UCS   from below

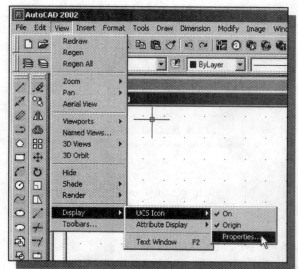

1. In the pull-down menus, select:

    **[View] → [Display] →
    [UCSIcon] → [Properties]**

2. In the *UCS* icon style section, switch to the **2D** option as shown.

3. Click **OK** to accept the settings.

❖ Note the **W** symbol in the *UCS* icon indicates the UCS is aligned to the world coordinate system.

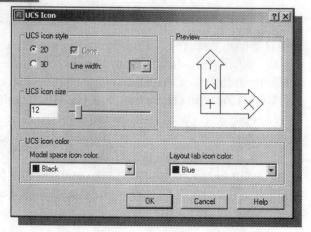

Cartesian and Polar Coordinate Systems

In a two-dimensional space, a point can be represented using different coordinate systems. The point can be located, using a *Cartesian coordinate system*, as X and Y units away from the origin. The same point can also be located using the *polar coordinate system*, as r and θ units away from the origin.

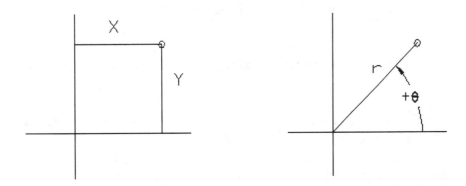

For planar geometry, the polar coordinate system is very useful for certain applications. In the polar coordinate system, points are defined in terms of a radial distance, r, from the origin and an angle θ between the direction of r and the positive X axis. The default system for measuring angles in **AutoCAD® 2002** defines positive angular values as counter-clockwise from the positive X-axis.

Absolute and Relative Coordinates

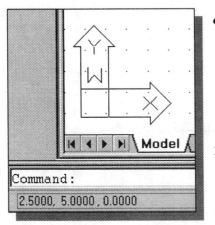

- **AutoCAD® 2002** also allows us to use *absolute* and *relative coordinates* to quickly construct objects. **Absolute coordinate values** are measured from the current coordinate system's origin point. **Relative coordinate values** are specified in relation to previous coordinates.

➤ Note that the *coordinate display area* can also be used as a toggle switch; each left-mouse-click will toggle the coordinate display *on* or *off*.

In **AutoCAD® 2002**, the *absolute* coordinates and the *relative* coordinates can be used in conjunction with the *Cartesian* and *polar* coordinate systems. By default, AutoCAD expects us to enter values in *absolute Cartesian coordinates*, distances measured from the current coordinate system's origin point. We can switch to using the *relative coordinates* by using the @ symbol. The @ symbol is used as the *relative coordinates specifier*, which means that we can specify the position of a point in relation to the previous point.

Defining Positions

In AutoCAD, there are five methods for specifying the locations of points when we create planar geometric entities.

➢ **Interactive method:** Use the cursor to select on the screen.

➢ **Absolute coordinates (Format: X,Y):** Type the X and Y coordinates to locate the point on the current coordinate system relative to the origin.

➢ **Relative rectangular coordinates (Format: @X,Y):** Type the X and Y coordinates relative to the last point.

➢ **Relative polar coordinates (Format: @Distance<angle):** Type a distance and angle relative to the last point.

➢ **Direct Distance entry technique**: Specify a second point by first moving the cursor to indicate direction and then entering a distance.

The *Guide Plate*

We will next create a mechanical design using the different coordinate entry methods.

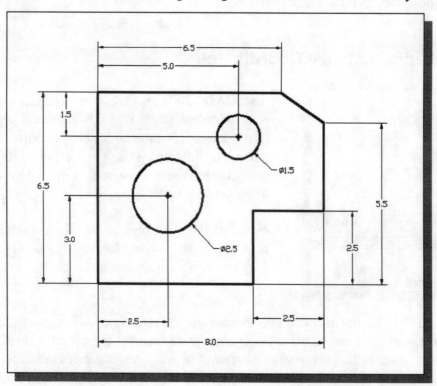

•   Use the *Erase* command and erase all entities on the screen before proceeding to the next section.

The rule for creating CAD designs and drawings is that they should be created at **full size** using real-world units. The CAD database contains all the definitions of the geometric entities and the design is considered as a virtual, full-sized object. Only when a printer or plotter transfers the CAD design to paper is the design scaled to fit on a sheet. The tedious task of determining a scale factor so that the design will fit on a sheet of paper is taken care of by the CAD system. This allows the designers and CAD operators to concentrate their attention on the more important issues – the design.

1. Select the **Line** command icon in the *Draw* toolbar. In the command prompt area, near the bottom of the AutoCAD graphics window, the message "*_line Specify first point:*" is displayed. AutoCAD expects us to identify the starting location of a straight line.

2. In the command prompt area, we will locate the starting point of our design at the origin of the *world coordinate system.*

   Command: _line Specify first point: **0,0 [ENTER]**
   (Type **0,0** in the command prompt area and press the [**ENTER**] key once.)

3. We will create a horizontal line by entering the absolute coordinates of the second point.

   Specify next point or [Undo]: **5.5,0 [ENTER]**

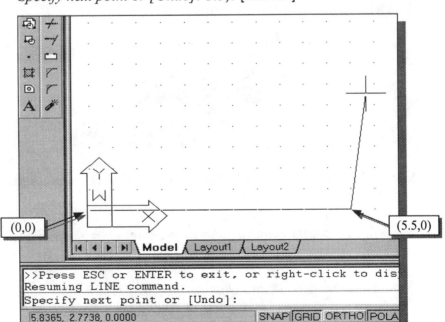

- The line we created is aligned to the bottom edge of the drawing window. Let us adjust the view of the line by using the *Pan Realtime* command.

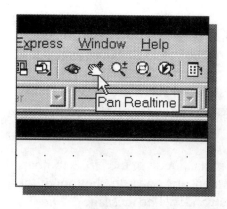

4. Click on the **Pan Realtime** icon in the *Standard* toolbar area. The icon is the picture of a hand with four arrows.

❖ The *Pan* command enables us to move the view to a different position. This function acts as if you are using a video camera.

5. Move the cursor, which appears as a hand inside the graphics window, near the center of the drawing window, then push down the left-mouse-button and drag the display toward the right and top side until we can see the sketched line. (Notice the scroll bars can also be used to adjust viewing of the display.)

6. Press the **[Esc]** key to exit the *Pan* command. Notice that AutoCAD goes back to the *Line* command.

7. We will create a vertical line by using the *relative rectangular coordinates entry method*, relative to the last point we specified:

Specify next point or [Close/Undo]: **@0,2.5** **[ENTER]**

8. We can mix any of the entry methods in positioning the locations of the endpoints. Move the cursor to the *Status Bar* area, and turn on the *GRID* and *SNAP* options.

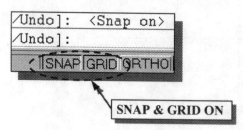

9. Create the next line by picking the location, world coordinates **(8,2.5),** on the screen.

10. We will next use the *relative polar coordinates entry method*, relative to the last point we specified:

Specify next point or [Close/Undo]: **@3<90** **[ENTER]**
(Distance is **3** inches with an angle of **90** degrees)

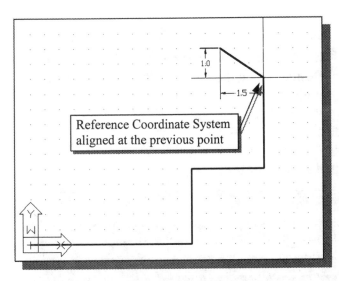

11. Using the *relative rectangular coordinates entry method* to create the next line, we can imagine a *reference coordinate system* aligned at the previous point. Coordinates are measured along the two reference axes.

Specify next point or [Close/Undo]: **@-1.5,1 [ENTER]**

(**-1.5** and **1** inches are measured relative to the reference point.)

12. Move the cursor directly to the left of the last point and use the *direct distance entry technique* by entering **6.5 [ENTER]**.

13. For the last segment of the sketch, we can use the **Close** option to connect back to the starting point. Inside the graphics window, **right-mouse-click** and a popup menu appears on the screen.

14. Select **Close** with the left-mouse-button to connect back to the starting point and end the *Line* command.

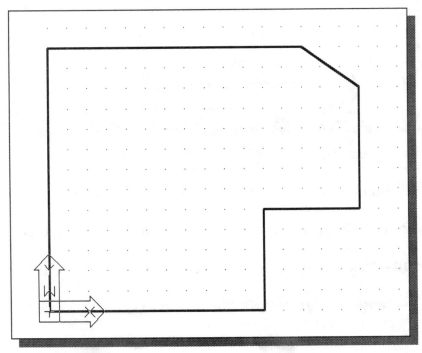

Creating *Circles*

The menus and toolbars in **AutoCAD® 2002** are designed to allow the CAD operators to quickly activate the desired commands. Besides using the *Draw* toolbar, we can also select the different *Draw* commands through the pull-down menus.

1.   In the pull-down menus, select:

[Draw] → [Circle] → [Center, Diameter]

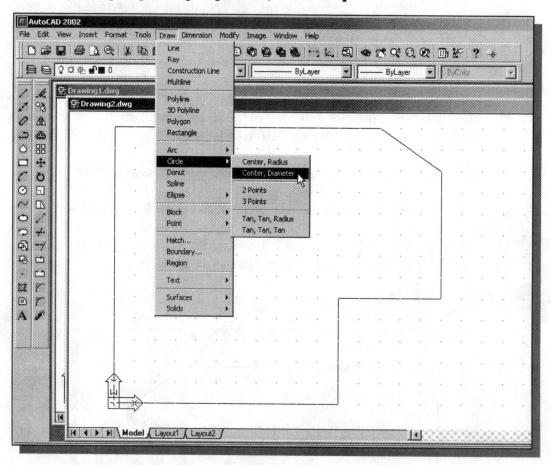

Notice the different options available under the circle submenu:

- **Center Point**: Draws a circle based on a center point and a diameter or a radius.

- **3 Points**: Draws a circle based on three points on the circumference.

- **2 Points**: Draws a circle based on two endpoints of the diameter.

- **TTR—Tangent, Tangent, Radius**: Draws a circle with a specified radius tangent to two objects.

- **TTT—Tangent, Tangent, Tangent**: Draws a circle tangent to three objects.

2. In the command prompt area, the message "*Specify center point for circle or [3P/2P/Ttr (tan tan radius)]:*" is displayed. AutoCAD expects us to identify the location of a point or enter an option. We can use any of the four coordinate entry methods to identify the desired location. We will enter the **world coordinates (2.5,3)** as the center point for the first circle.

Specify center point for circle or [3P/2P/Ttr (tan tan radius)]: **2.5,3 [ENTER]**

3. In the command prompt area, the message "*Specify diameter of circle:*" is displayed.

Specify diameter of circle: **2.5 [ENTER]**

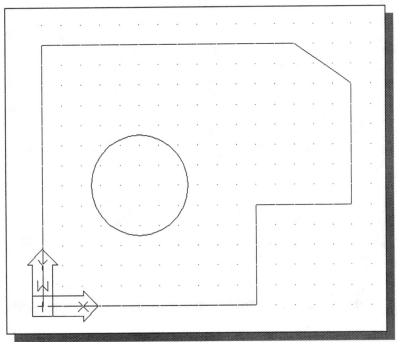

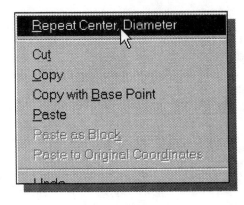

4. Inside the graphics window, **right-mouse-click** to bring up the popup option menu.

5. Pick **Repeat Center, Diameter** with the left-mouse-button in the popup menu to repeat the last command.

6. Using the *relative rectangular coordinates entry method*, relative to the center-point coordinates of the first circle, we specify the location as **(2.5,2)**.

Specify center point for circle or [3P/2P/Ttr (tan tan radius)]: **@2.5,2 [ENTER]**

7. In the command prompt area, the message "*Specify Diameter of circle: <2.50>*" is displayed. The default option for the *Circle* command in AutoCAD is to specify the *radius* and the last radius used is also displayed in brackets.

Specify Diameter of circle<2.50>: **1.5 [ENTER]**

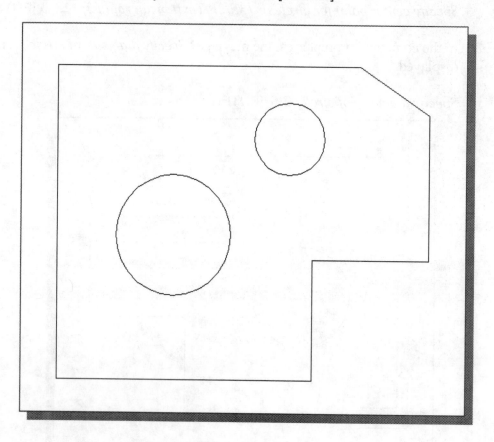

Saving the CAD Design

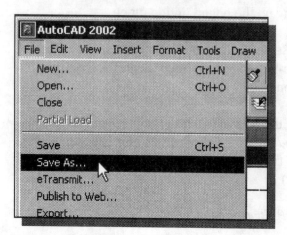

1. In the pull-down menus, select:

   [File] → [Save As]

2. In the *Save Drawing As* dialog box, select the folder in which you want to store the CAD file and enter **GuidePlate** in the *File name* box.

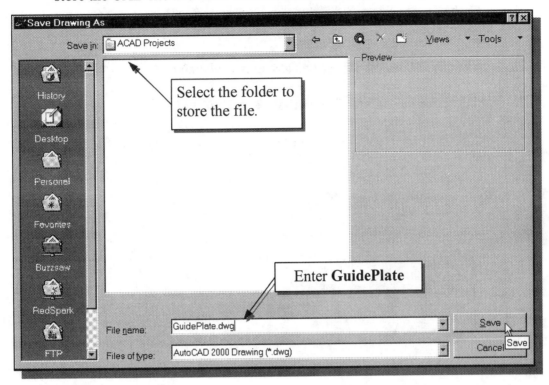

3. Pick **Save** in the *Save Drawing As* dialog box to accept the selections and save the file.

Exit AutoCAD 2002

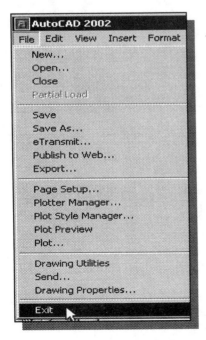

❖ To exit **AutoCAD® 2002**, select **File** then choose **Exit** from the pull-down menu or type *QUIT* at the command prompt.

Questions:

1. What are the advantages and disadvantages of using CAD systems to create engineering drawings?

2. How do the *GRID* and *SNAP* options assist us in sketching?

3. List and describe the different **coordinate entry methods** available in AutoCAD?

4. List and describe two types of coordinate systems commonly used for planar geometry.

5. Identify the following commands:

(a)

(b)

(c)

(d)

Tan, Tan, Radius

Exercises: (All dimensions are in inches.)

1.

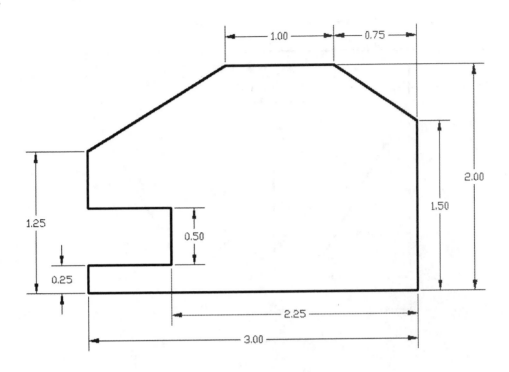

2.

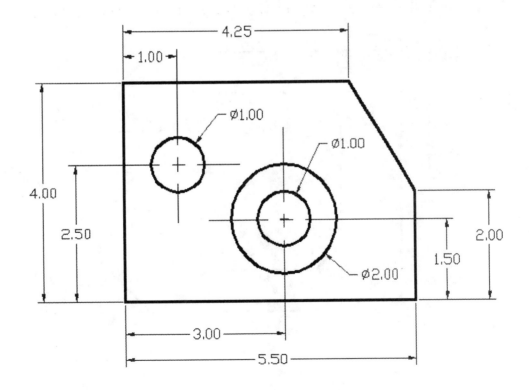

3.

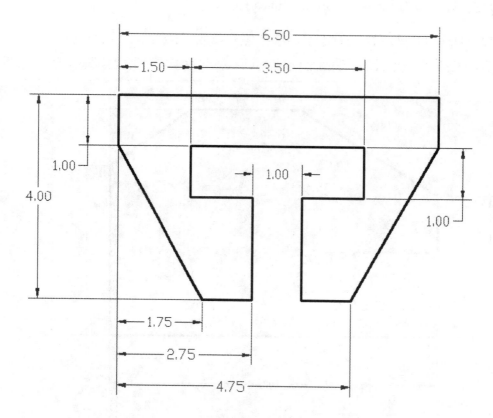

4.

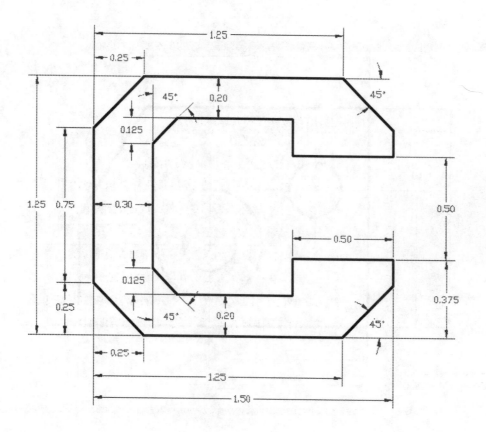

Lesson 3
Geometric Construction and Editing Tools

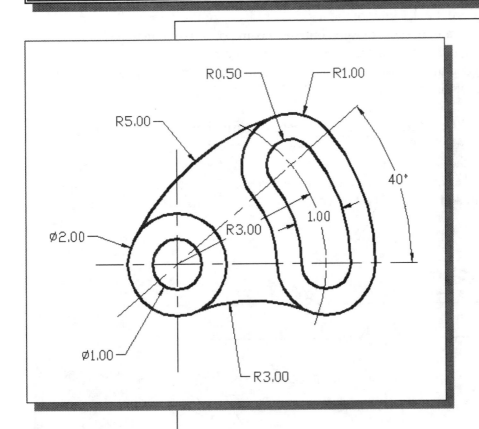

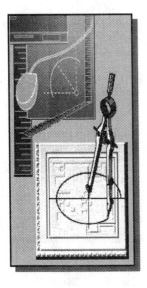

Learning Objectives

- ♦ Set up Drawing Units.
- ♦ Set up GRID & SNAP intervals.
- ♦ Display AutoCAD's Toolbars.
- ♦ Set up and use OBJECT SNAPS.
- ♦ Edit, using EXTEND and TRIM.
- ♦ Use the FILLET command.
- ♦ Create parallel geometric entities.
- ♦ Use the EXPLODE command.

Introduction

The main characteristic of any CAD system is its ability to create and modify geometric entities quickly and accurately. Most CAD systems provide a variety of construction and editing tools to relieve the designer of the tedious drudgery of this task, so that the designer can concentrate more on design content. It is important to note that CAD systems can be used to replace the traditional drafting with pencil and paper, but the CAD user must have a good understanding of the basic geometric construction techniques to fully utilize the capability of the CAD systems.

In this lesson, we will examine the basic geometric construction and editing tools provided by **AutoCAD® 2002**. We will first look at tools such as *UNITS*, *GRID*, *SNAP* intervals setup and the *OSNAP* option, followed by editing tools such as *Trim*, *Extend*, *Fillet*, *Pedit* and *Offset*. We will illustrate the basic geometric construction and editing options available in **AutoCAD® 2002** by constructing the *Gasket* design, as shown in the below figure.

The *Gasket* Project:

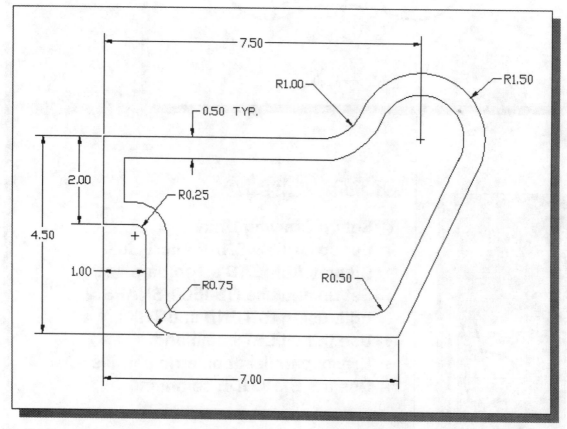

❖ Before continuing to the next page, on your own make a rough sketch showing the steps that can be used to create the design. Be aware that there are many different approaches to accomplishing the same task.

Starting Up AutoCAD® 2002

1. Select the **AutoCAD 2002** option on the *Program* menu or select the **AutoCAD 2002** icon on the *Desktop*. Once the program is loaded into the memory, the **AutoCAD® 2002** drawing screen and the *AutoCAD Today* startup dialog box will appear on the screen.

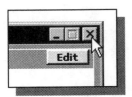

2. In the *AutoCAD 2002 Today* startup dialog box, close the dialog box by clicking the **Close** icon with a single click of the left-mouse-button.

❖ Note the units setting of *Drawing1* is set to the default system units. **AutoCAD® 2002** provides several options to control the units' settings. In the next section, we will illustrate the *Units* command to examine and/or modify the units settings.

Drawing Units Setup

Every object we construct in a CAD system is measured in units. We should determine the value of the units within the CAD system before creating the first geometric entities. For example, in one drawing, a unit might equal one millimeter of the real-world object. In another drawing, a unit might equal an inch. We can set the unit type and number of decimal places for object lengths and angles. In AutoCAD, *drawing units settings* control how AutoCAD interprets the coordinate and angle entries and how it displays coordinates and units in the *Status Bar* and in the dialog boxes. Setting the drawing units does not automatically set the units for dimensions. We generally set drawing units and dimension units to the same type and precision, but AutoCAD allows us to set different values for dimension units.

1. In the pull-down menus, select:

   [Format] → **[Units]**

2. In the *Drawing Units* dialog box, set the *Length Type* to **Decimal**. This will set the measurement to the default English units, inches.

3. Set the *Precision* to **two digits** after the decimal point.

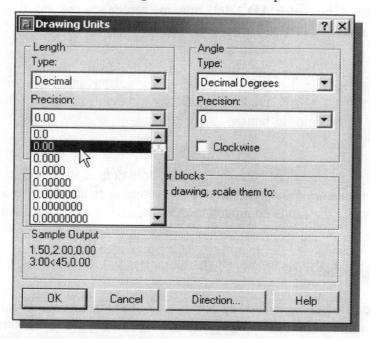

4. Pick **OK** to exit the *Drawing Units* dialog box.

GRID and SNAP intervals Setup

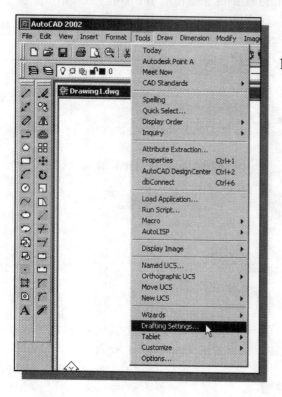

1. In the pull-down menus, select:

    [Tools] → [Drafting Settings]

2. In the *Drafting Settings* dialog box, select the **Snap and Grid** tab if it is not the page on top.

3. Change *Grid Spacing* to **1.00** for both X and Y directions.

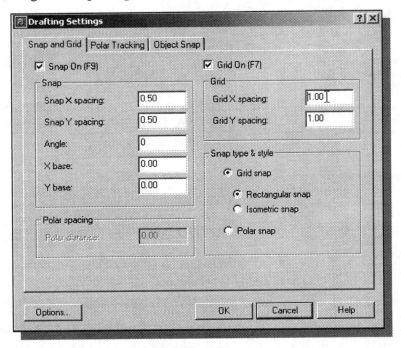

4. Switch on the *Grid On* and *Snap On* options if they are not already switched on.

5. Pick **OK** to exit the *Drawing Units* dialog box.

❖ Notice in the *Status Bar* area, the *GRID* and *SNAP* options are pressed down indicating they are switched *on*. The grid spacing is set to 1 inch and the snap interval is set to 0.5 inch.

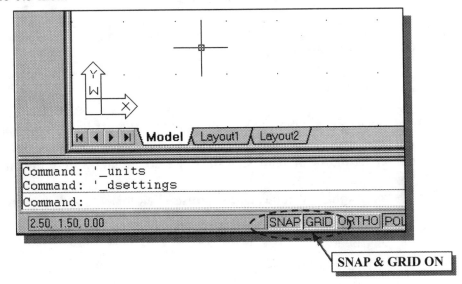

Using the *Line* command

1. Select the **Line** command icon in the *Draw* toolbar. In the command prompt area, near the bottom of the AutoCAD drawing screen, the message "*_line Specify first point:*" is displayed. AutoCAD expects us to identify the starting location of a straight line.

2. In the graphics window, move the cursor to **world coordinates (2,6). Left-click** to position the starting point of the line at that location.

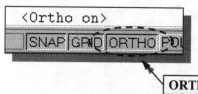

3. We will next turn on the *ORTHO* option by toggling on the **ORTHO** button in the *Status Bar* area.

❖ The *ORTHO* option constrains cursor movement to the horizontal or vertical directions, relative to the current coordinate system. With the *Line* command, we are now restricted to creating only horizontal or vertical lines with the *ORTHO* option.

4. Move the graphics cursor below the last point we selected on the screen and create a vertical line that is two units long (*Y coordinate: 4.00*).

5. Move the graphics cursor to the right of the last point and create a horizontal line that is one unit long (*X coordinate: 3.00*).

6. Move the graphics cursor below the last point and create a vertical line that is 2.5 units long (*Y coordinate: 1.50*).

7. **Turn OFF** the *SNAP* option in the *Status Bar* area.

8. Move the graphics cursor to the right of the last point and create a horizontal line that is about seven units long (near *X coordinate: 10.00*). As it is quite common during the initial design stage, we do not know all of the dimensions.

9. Inside the graphics window, **right-mouse-click** to activate the option menu and select **Enter** with the left-mouse-button to end the *Line* command.

10. In the *Status Bar* area, reset the option buttons so that only the *GRID*, *ORTHO*, and *MODEL* options are switched **ON**.

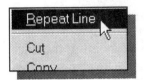

11. Activate the **Line** command by picking the icon in the *Draw* toolbar or **right-mouse-click** to activate the option menu and select **Repeat Line**.

Object Snap Toolbar

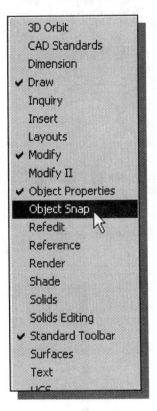

1. Move the cursor to the *Standard* toolbar area and **right-mouse-click** once on any icon in the toolbar area to display a list of toolbar menu groups.

   ❖ AutoCAD provides 24 toolbars for access to frequently used commands, settings, and modes. The *Standard*, *Object Properties*, *Draw*, and *Modify* toolbars are displayed by default. The *check marks* in the list identify the toolbars that are currently displayed on the screen.

2. Select **Object Snap**, with the left-mouse-button, to display the *Object Snap* toolbar on the screen.

   ❖ **Object Snap** is an extremely powerful construction tool available on most CAD systems. During an entity's creation operations, we can snap the cursor to points on objects such as endpoints, midpoints, centers, and intersections. For example, we can turn on **Object Snap** and quickly draw a line to the center of a circle, the midpoint of a line segment, or the intersection of two lines.

3. Move the cursor over the icons in the *Object Snap* toolbar and read the description of each icon in the *Status Bar* area.

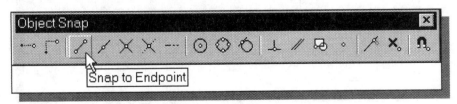

4. In the *Object Snap* toolbar, pick **Snap to Endpoint**. In the command prompt area, the message "*_endp of*" is displayed. AutoCAD now expects us to select a geometric entity on the screen.

> ❖ The *Snap to Endpoint* option allows us to snap to the closest endpoint of objects such as lines or arcs. AutoCAD uses the midpoint of the entity to determine which end to snap to.

5. Pick the **top-left vertical line** by selecting a location above the midpoint of the line. Notice AutoCAD automatically snaps to the top endpoint of the line.

6. Move the graphics cursor to the right of the last point and create a horizontal line that is about three units long (near *X coordinate: 5.00*).

7. Inside the graphics window, **right-mouse-click** to activate the option menu and select **Enter** with the left-mouse-button to end the *Line* command.

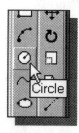

8. Select the **Circle** command icon in the *Draw* toolbar. In the command prompt area, the message "*Specify center point for circle or [3P/2P/Ttr (tan tan radius)]:*" is displayed.

9. In the *Status Bar* area, switch **ON** the *SNAP* option.

10. In the graphics window, move the cursor to world coordinates **(9.5,6). Left-click** to position the center point of the circle at this location.

11. Move the graphics cursor to world coordinates **(11,6). Left-click** at this location to create a circle (radius 1.5 inches).

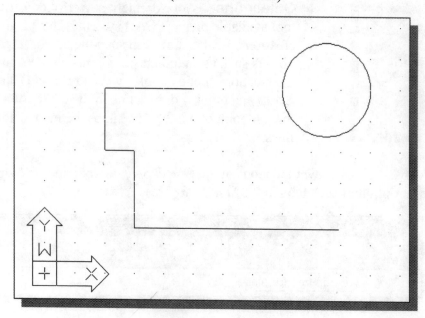

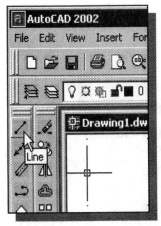

12. Select the **Line** command icon in the *Draw* toolbar. In the command prompt area, the message "*_line Specify first point:*" is displayed.

13. In the graphics window, move the cursor to world coordinates **(9,1.5)**. **Left-click** to position the first point of a line at this location.

14. Pick **Snap to Tangent** in the *Object Snap* toolbar. In the command prompt area, the message "*_tan to*" is displayed. AutoCAD now expects us to select a circle or an arc on the screen.

❖ The **Snap to Tangent** option allows us to snap to the point on a circle or arc that, when connected to the last point, forms a line tangent to that object.

15. Pick a location on the right side of the circle and create the line tangent to the circle. Note that the *Object Snap* options take precedence over the *ORTHO* option.

16. Inside the graphics window, **right-mouse-click** to activate the option menu and select **Enter** with the left-mouse-button to end the *Line* command.

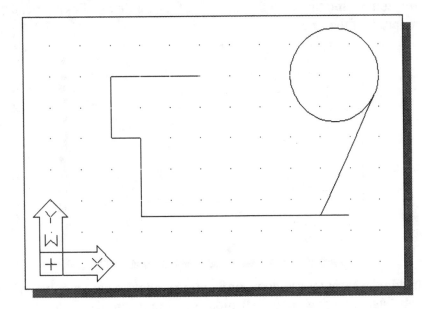

17. In the *Status Bar* area, reset the option buttons so that only the *MODEL* button is switched *ON*.

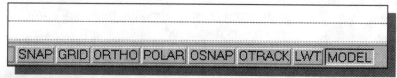

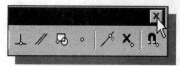

18. Close the *Object Snap* toolbar by **left-clicking** the upper right corner X icon.

Using the *Extend* command

- The *Extend* command lengthens an object so that it ends precisely at a selected boundary.

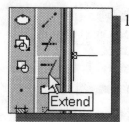

1. Select the **Extend** command icon in the *Modify* toolbar. In the command prompt area, the message "*Select boundary edges... Select objects:*" is displayed.

   ❖ First we will select the objects that define the boundary edges to which we want to extend the object.

2. Pick the **circle** as the *boundary edge*.

3. Inside the graphics window, **right-mouse-click** to proceed with the *Extend* command.

4. The message "*Select object to extend or shift-select object to trim or [Project/Edge/Undo]:*" is displayed in the command prompt area. Extend the **horizontal line** that is to the left side of the circle by clicking near the right-endpoint of the line.

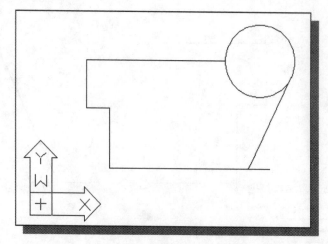

5. Inside the graphics window, **right-mouse-click** to activate the option menu and select **Enter** with the left-mouse-button to end the *Extend* command.

Using the *Trim* Command

- The *Trim* command shortens an object so that it ends precisely at a selected boundary.

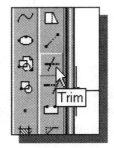

1. Select the **Trim** command icon in the *Modify* toolbar. In the command prompt area, the message *"Select boundary edges... Select objects:"* is displayed.

   - First we will select the objects that define the boundary edges to which we want to trim the object.

2. Pick the inclined line and the top horizontal line as the *boundary edges*.

3. Inside the graphics window, **right-mouse-click** to proceed with the *Trim* command.

4. The message *"Select object to trim or shift-select object to extend or [Project/Edge/Undo]:"* is displayed in the command prompt area. Pick the right endpoint of the bottom horizontal line.

5. Pick the bottom of the circle by clicking on the lower portion of the circle.

6. Inside the graphics window, **right-mouse-click** to activate the option menu and select **Enter** with the left-mouse-button to end the *Trim* command.

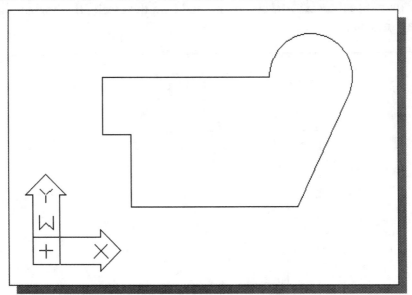

- Note that in **AutoCAD® 2002**, we can perform either trimming or extending an object using the *Extend* command or the *Trim* command. For example, when using the **Extend** command, we can select an object to *extend* or hold down **SHIFT** and select an object to *trim*.

Creating a *TTR circle*

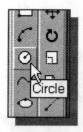

1. Select the **Circle** command icon in the *Draw* toolbar. In the command prompt area, the message "*Specify center point for circle or [3P/2P/Ttr (tan tan radius)]:*" is displayed.

2. Inside the graphics window, **right-mouse-click** to activate the option menu and select the **Ttr (Tan Tan Radius)** option. This option allows us to create a circle that is tangent to two objects.

3. Pick the **top horizontal line** that is to the left side of the arc. We will create a circle that is tangent to this line and the circle.

4. Pick the **circle** by selecting a location that is above the right endpoint of the horizontal line. AutoCAD interprets the location we selected as being near the tangency.

5. In the command prompt area, the message "*Specify radius of circle <1.50>*" is displayed.

    Specify radius of circle <1.50>: **1.0** **[ENTER]**

➤ On your own, use the **Extend** command and trim the circle, the horizontal line, and the arc as shown.

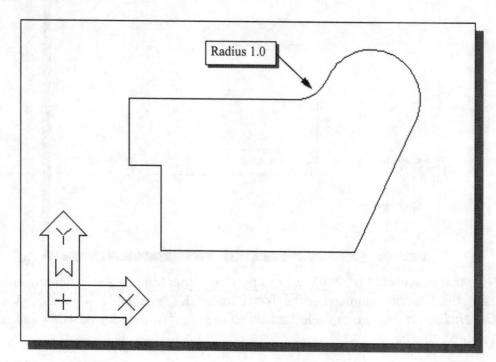

Using the *Fillet* command

- *Fillet* rounds or fillets the edges of two arcs, circles, elliptical arcs, or lines with an arc of a specified radius.

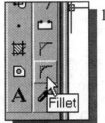

1. Select the **Fillet** command icon in the *Modify* toolbar. In the command prompt area, the message "*Select first object or [Polyline/Radius/Trim]:*" is displayed.

2. Inside the graphics window, **right-mouse-click** to activate the option menu and select the **Radius** option with the left-mouse-button to specify the radius of the fillet.

3. In the command prompt area, the message "*Specify fillet radius:*" is displayed.

   Specify fillet radius: **0.75 [ENTER]**

4. Pick the **bottom horizontal line** and the **adjacent vertical line** to create a rounded corner as shown.

➢ On your own, use the *Fillet* command and create a 0.25 fillet at the corner as shown.

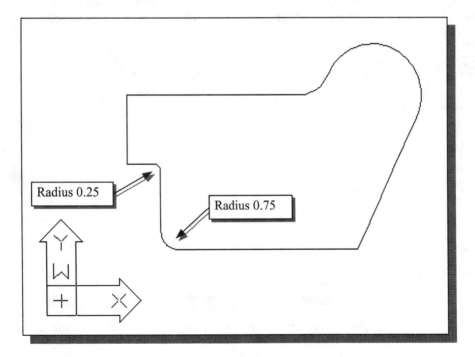

Converting objects into a Polyline

- The next task in our project is to use the *Offset* command and create a scaled copy of the constructed geometry. Prior to using the *Offset* command, we will simplify the procedure by converting all objects into a **compound object – a** *polyline*.

❖ A *polyline* in AutoCAD is a 2D line of adjustable width composed of line and arc segments. A polyline is treated as a single object with definable options.

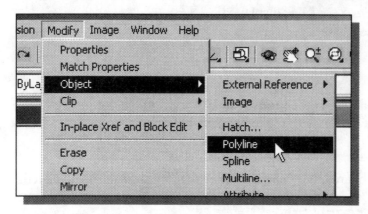

1. In the pull-down menus, select:

   [Modify] → [Object] → [Polyline]

2. The message "*Select polyline:*" is displayed in the command prompt area. Select any of the objects on the screen.

3. The message "*Object selected is not a polyline, Do you want to turn it into one? <Y>*" is displayed in the command prompt area. **Right-mouse-click** to accept the *Yes* default.

4. Inside the graphics window, **right-mouse-click** to activate the option menu and select the **Join** option with the left-mouse-button to add objects to the polyline.

5. **Pick all objects** by enclosing them inside a *selection window*.

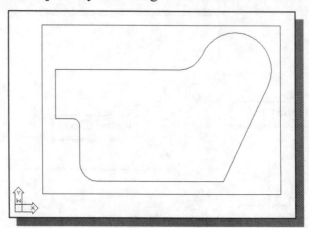

6. Inside the graphics window, **right-mouse-click** to accept the selected objects.

7. Inside the graphics window, **right-mouse-click** to activate the option menu and select **Enter** to end the *Pedit* command.

Using the *Offset* command

* The *Offset* command creates a new object at a specified distance from an existing object or through a specified point.

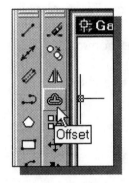

1. Select the **Offset** command icon in the *Modify* toolbar. In the command prompt area, the message *"Specify offset distance or [Through]:"* is displayed.

    Specify offset distance or [Through]: **0.5 [ENTER]**

2. In the command prompt area, the message *"Select object to offset or <exit>:"* is displayed. Pick any object on the screen.

3. Since all the lines and arcs have been converted into a single object, all segments are selected.

4. AutoCAD next asks us to identify the direction of the offset. Pick a location that is *inside* the polyline.

5. Inside the graphics window, **right-mouse-click** to end the *Offset* command.

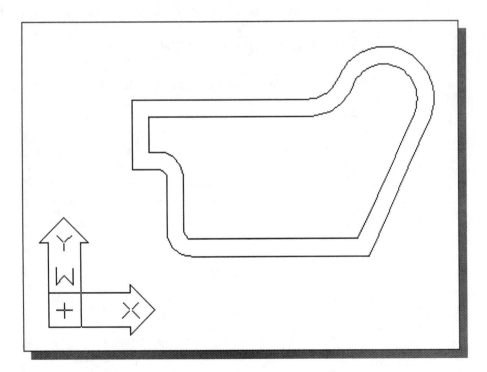

Using the *Explode* command

- The **Explode** command breaks a compound object into its component objects.

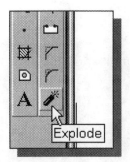

1. Select the **Explode** command icon in the *Modify* toolbar. In the command prompt area, the message "*Select objects:*" is displayed.

2. Pick the *polyline* that we created using the **Offset** command.

3. Inside the graphics window, **right-mouse-click** to end the *Explode* command.

Create another *Fillet*

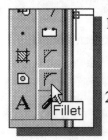

1. Select the **Fillet** command icon in the *Modify* toolbar. In the command prompt area, the message "*Select first object or [Polyline/Radius/Trim]:*" is displayed.

2. Inside the graphics window, **right-mouse-click** to activate the option menu and select the **Radius** option with the left-mouse-button to specify the radius of the fillet.

3. In the command prompt area, the message "*Specify fillet radius:*" is displayed.

   Specify fillet radius: **0.5 [ENTER]**

4. Pick the **horizontal line** and the **adjacent inclined line** to create a rounded corner as shown.

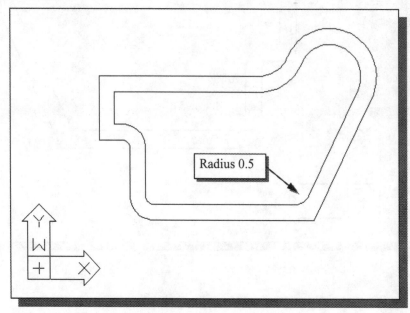

Saving the Design

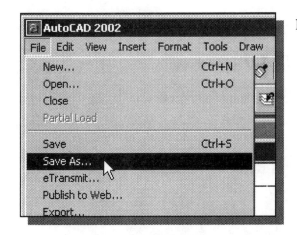

1. In the pull-down menus, select:

   [File] → [Save As]

2. In the *Save Drawing As* dialog box, select the folder in which you want to store the CAD file and enter *Gasket* in the *File name* box.

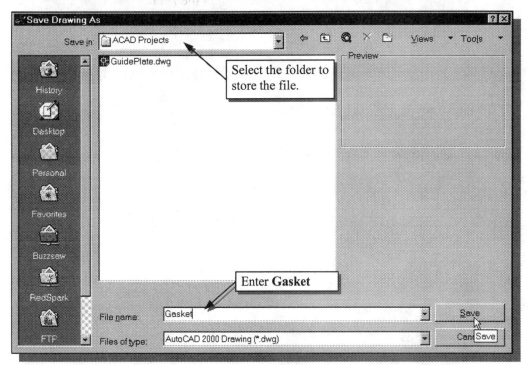

3. Pick **Save** in the *Save Drawing As* dialog box to accept the selections and save the file.

Exit AutoCAD

- To exit **AutoCAD® 2002**, select **File** then choose **Exit** from the pull-down menu or type *QUIT* at the command prompt.

Questions:

1. Describe the AutoCAD **ORTHO** option.

2. List and describe three AutoCAD **OBJECT SNAP** options.

3. Which AutoCAD command can we use to create rounded corners?

4. Describe the AutoCAD **Offset** command.

5. Identify the following commands:

(a)

(b)

(c)

(d)

Exercises: Unless otherwise specified, dimensions are in inches.

1.

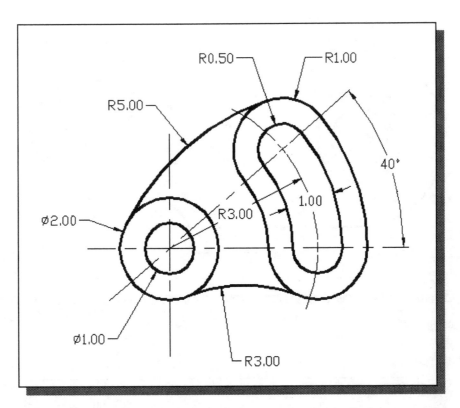

2.   (Note: This design has two sets of parallel lines with implied tangency.)

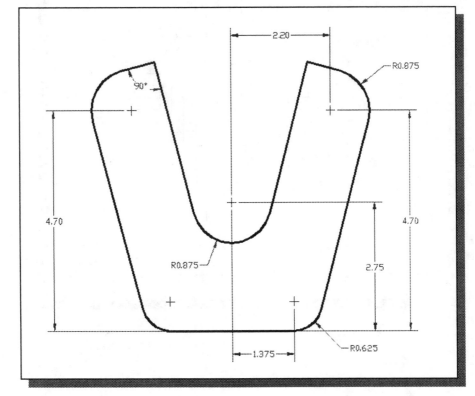

3. Dimensions are in Millimeters.

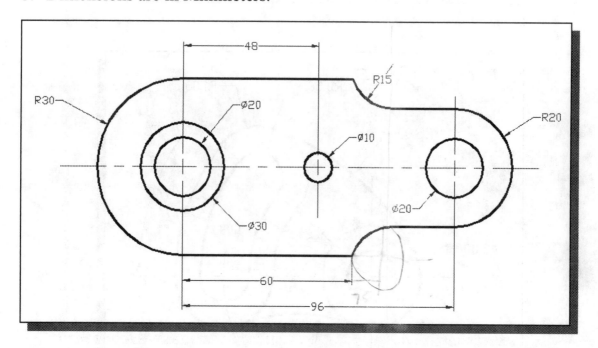

4.

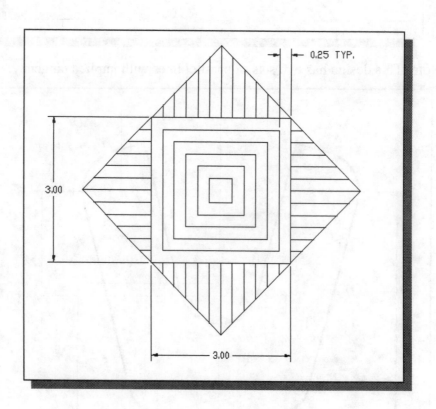

5.

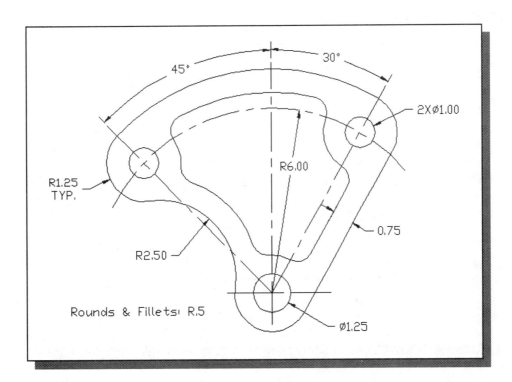

6.

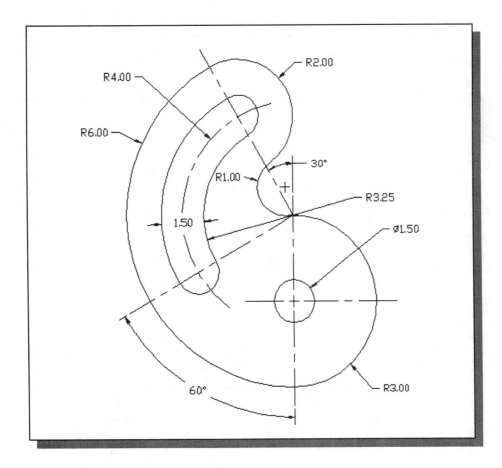

Notes:

Lesson 4
Object Properties and Organization

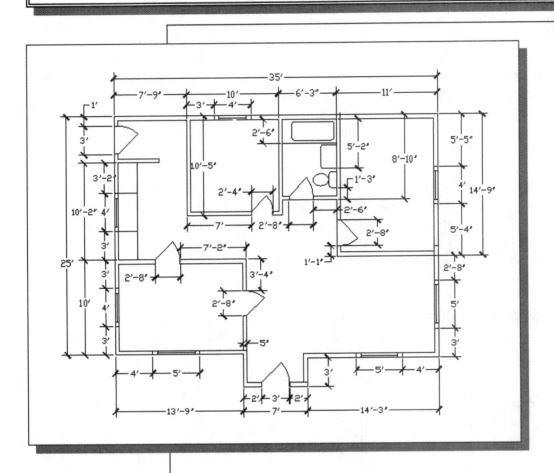

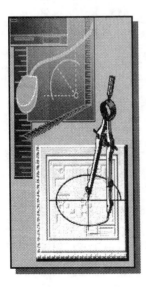

Learning Objectives

♦ **Using the AutoCAD Quick Setup wizard.**
♦ **Create new Multiline Styles.**
♦ **Draw, using the MULTILINE command.**
♦ **Use the ZOOM ALL command.**
♦ **Create new layers.**
♦ **Pre-selection of objects.**
♦ **Controlling Layer Visibility.**
♦ **Moving objects to a different layer.**

Introduction

The CAD database of a design may contain information regarding the hundreds of CAD entities that are used to create the CAD model. One of the advantages of using a CAD system is its ability to organize and manage the database so that the designer can access the information quickly and easily. Typically, CAD entities that are created to describe one feature, function, or process of a design are perceived as related information and therefore are organized into the same group. In AutoCAD, the **Layer** command is used extensively for this purpose. For example, an architectural drawing typically will show walls, doors, windows, and dimensions. Using layers, we can choose to display or hide sub-systems for clarity; we can also change object properties, such as colors and linetypes, quickly and easily.

In this lesson, we will continue to explore the different construction and editing tools that are available in **AutoCAD® 2002**. We will demonstrate the use of the *Limits*, *Mline*, *Medit*, and *Layer* commands. As you become proficient with the CAD tools and understand the underlying CAD modeling concepts, you are encouraged to experiment with new ideas in using the CAD tools and develop your own style of using the system.

The *Floor Plan* Design

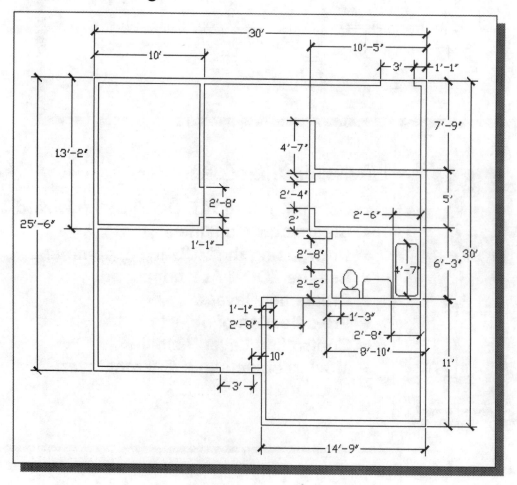

Starting Up AutoCAD® 2002

1. Select the **AutoCAD 2002** option on the *Program* menu or select the **AutoCAD 2002** icon on the *Desktop*. Once the program is loaded into the memory, the **AutoCAD® 2002** drawing screen and the *AutoCAD 2002 Today* startup dialog box will appear on the screen.

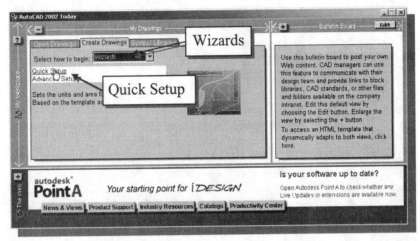

2. In the *AutoCAD 2002 Today* startup dialog box, select the **Create Drawings** tab with a single click of the left-mouse-button.

3. In the startup dialog box, select the **Wizards** option as shown in the above figure.

4. In the *Wizards* section, pick **Quick Setup**.

- AutoCAD setup wizards allow us to customize several of the AutoCAD settings depending on the wizard we choose. The *Quick Setup* wizard sets the units and grid display area. Choices for units include *Decimal, Engineering, Architectural, Fractional,* and *Scientific.* We can also specify the width and length of a two-dimensional area to establish the extents of the *grid* displayed, also known as the *limits* of the working area.

Drawing Units Setup

1. In the *Quick Setup Units* option, select **Architectural**.

2. Pick **Next** to continue with the *Quick Setup* settings.

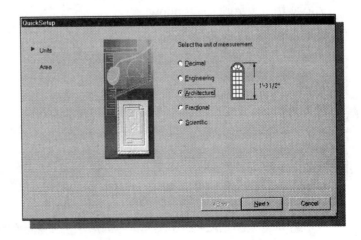

Reference Area Setup

1. In the *Quick Setup Area* option, enter **60'** and **40'** for the width and length.

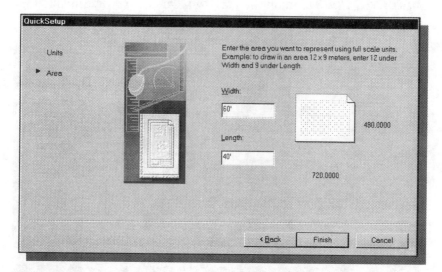

- The two-dimensional area we set up in the *Quick Setup* is called the *limits* in AutoCAD. Setting the *limits* controls the extents of the display of the *grid*, and also provides the following functionality:

  - Serves as a visual reference that marks the working area.

  - Serves as a tool that can be used to prevent construction outside the grid limits.

  - Serves as a plot option that defines an area to be plotted/printed.

2. Pick **Finish** to accept the settings and end the *Quick Setup* wizard.

- We have two drawing windows opened in the AutoCAD screen window. Note that the units setting of *Drawing1* is set to the default system units. The *Drawing2* window is set up through the AutoCAD *Quick Setup* wizard, which sets the units to the architectural style. To avoid any confusion in following through the tutorial, let's close the *Drawing1* window.

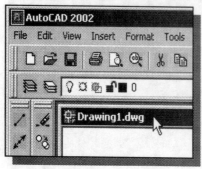

3. Switch to the *Drawing1* window by left-clicking once in the title area of the window.

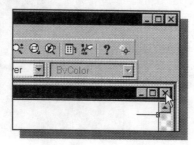

4. Close the window by clicking the ***Close*** icon located at the upper-right-corner of the *Drawing1* window.

GRID and *SNAP* intervals Setup

1. In the pull-down menus, select:
   [Tools] → [Drafting Settings]

2. In the *Drafting Settings* dialog box, select the
   SNAP and GRID tab if it is not the page on top.

3. Change *Grid Spacing* to *6″* for both X and Y
   directions.

4. Also adjust the *Snap Spacing* to *6″* for both X and
   Y directions.

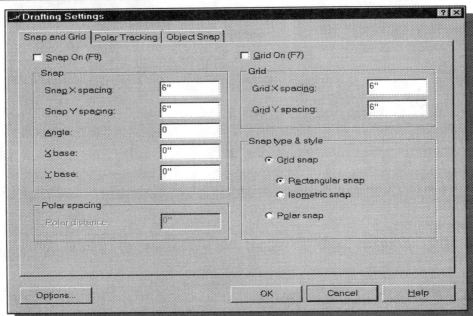

5. Pick **OK** to exit the *Drafting Settings* dialog box.

6. In the *Status Bar* area, reset the option buttons so that only *SNAP, GRID*, and
   MODEL are switched *ON*.

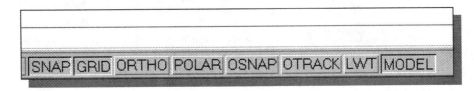

Using the *Zoom All* command

1. Move the cursor inside the graphics window and notice that, although we have set the *limits* to 40' by 60', the default display is still 9" by 12". In the graphics window, only a few grid points are displayed.

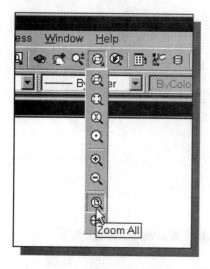

2. In the *Standard* toolbar area, click and hold down the **Zoom Window** button, and the list of available *Zoom* options appears. Move the cursor over the different icons and read the brief description of each icon to get a feel for what each option does.

3. Move the cursor over the **Zoom All** icon, the second icon from the bottom of the list, and release the left-mouse-button to select the command.

The *Zoom All* command displays all objects in the current design. In a two-dimensional view, AutoCAD zooms to the drawing limits or the area that shows all objects, whichever is greater.

The AutoCAD *Multiline* command

- The **Multiline** command in **AutoCAD® 2002** is used to create multiple parallel lines. This command is very useful for creating designs that contain multiple parallel lines, such as walls for architectural designs and for highway designs in civil engineering. The *Multiline* command creates a set of parallel lines and all line segments are grouped together to form a single *multiline object*, which can be modified using *Multiline Edit* and *Explode* commands. We will first create a new **multiline style** for our floor plan design.

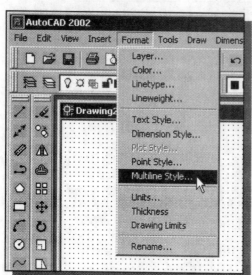

1. In the pull-down menus, select:

   [Format] → [Multiline Style]

❖ The default AutoCAD multiline style is called *STANDARD*, and it consists of two elements (two parallel lines) with an offset distance of 10 inches.

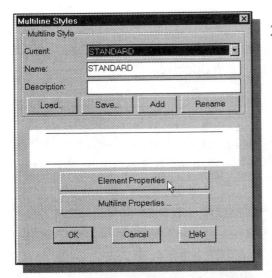

2. In the *Multiline Styles* dialog box choose **Element Properties**.

❖ In the *Element Properties* dialog box, all the line elements in the current multiline style are displayed. Each line element in the style is defined by its offset from a reference line, the *multiline origin*.

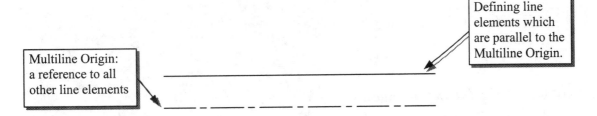

Defining line elements which are parallel to the Multiline Origin.

Multiline Origin: a reference to all other line elements

❖ Note that, in the *Element Properties* dialog box, all the line elements are listed in descending order with respect to their offsets. We will create two line elements representing a five-inch wall.

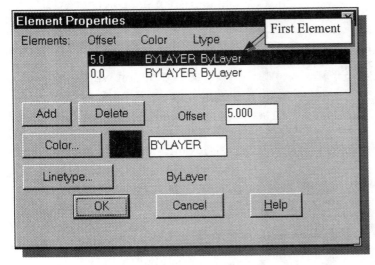

First Element

3. In the *Element Properties* dialog box, highlight the first element in the list, and change the *Offset* to **5.0**.

4. Pick the *second element* in the *Element Properties* dialog box and change the *Offset* to **0.0**.

5. Choose **OK** to exit the *Element Properties* dialog box.

❖ Notice the *Add* and *Delete* options are also available in the dialog box, which allow us to create or remove as many as 16 elements in a multiline style.

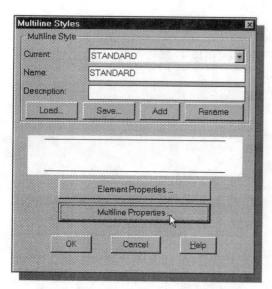

6. In the *Multiline Styles* dialog box choose **Multiline Properties**.

7. In the *Multiline Properties* dialog box, **left-click** the *Start* and *End* boxes to enable the *Line end-caps*.

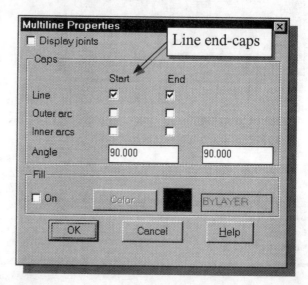

8. Choose **OK** to exit the *Multiline Properties* dialog box.

9. In the *Multiline Styles* dialog box; in the *Name* box, enter *WALL* as the new *Multiline Style* name.

10. Enter *5" wall with line endcaps* in the *Description* box.

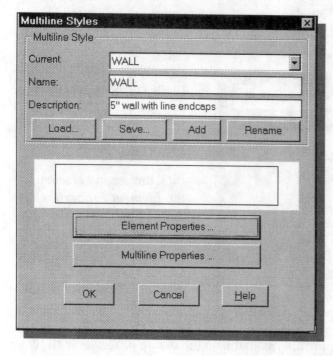

11. Left-click the **Add** button to add the new multiline style to the database of the current CAD design. (The *Current Multiline style* is set to *WALL* as shown.)

    The **Save** button will save a multiline style to the library of multiline styles. By default, AutoCAD saves the multiline styles information to a file called **acad.mln**. The **Load** button allows us to retrieve multiline styles from a library.

12. Choose **OK** to exit the *Multiline Styles* dialog box.

Drawing Multilines

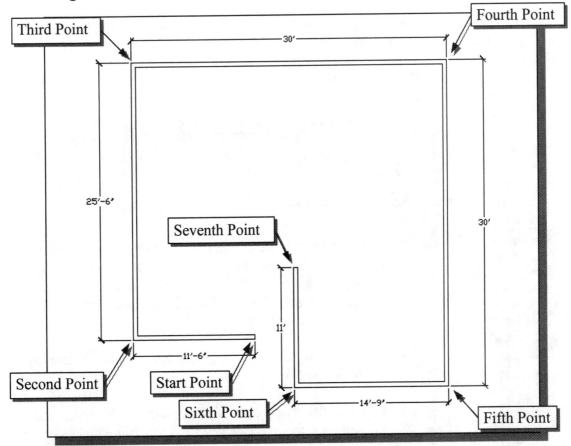

Third Point
Fourth Point
30'
25'-6'
30'
Seventh Point
11'
Second Point
11'-6'
Start Point
14'-9'
Sixth Point
Fifth Point

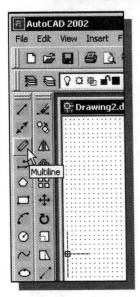

1. Select the **Multiline** command icon in the *Draw* toolbar. In the text window, the current settings "*Justification = Top, Scale = 1.00, Style = Wall*" are displayed.

2. In the command prompt area, the message "*Specify start point or [Justification/Scale/Style]:*" is displayed. AutoCAD expects us to identify the starting location or adjust any of the settings. Select a location near the bottom of the graphics window as the **start point** of the multiline by left-clicking the mouse.

3. In the command prompt area, create a vertical line by using the *relative rectangular coordinates entry method*, relative to the last point we specified

    Specify next point: **@-11'6",0 [ENTER]**

4. On your own, complete the multiline by specifying the points, *point three* through *point seven*, as shown.

5. Inside the graphics window, right-mouse-click and select **Enter** to end the *Multiline* command.

Creating interior walls

1. Move the cursor on any icon in the *Standard* toolbar area and **right-mouse-click** once to display a list of toolbar menu groups.

2. Select **Object Snap**, with the left-mouse-button, to display the *Object Snap* toolbar on the screen to assist the construction of the floor plan.

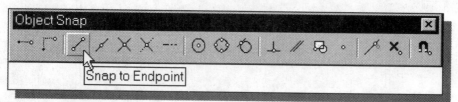

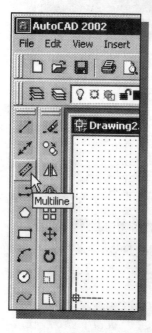

3. Select the ***Multiline*** command icon in the *Draw* toolbar. In the text window, the current settings "*Justification = Top, Scale = 1.00, Style = Wall*" are displayed. In the command prompt area, the message "*Specify start point or [Justification/Scale/Style]:*" is displayed.

4. Inside the graphics window, **right-mouse-click** to display the option menu.

5. Pick **Justification** in the option menu. In the command prompt area, the message "*Enter justification type [Top/Zero/Bottom] <Top>:*" is displayed.

6. Inside the graphics window, right-mouse-click to display the option menu and select **Bottom** so that the points we select will align to the bottom element.

7. In the *Object Snap* toolbar, pick ***Snap to Midpoint***. In the command prompt area, the message "*_mid of*" is displayed. AutoCAD now expects us to select a geometric entity on the screen.

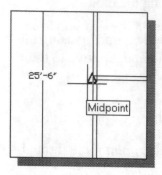

8. Select the vertical line on the left as shown.

9. At the command prompt, enter **@10',0 [ENTER]**.

10. Now enter **@0,1'1"**, to define the vertical stub wall.

11. Inside the graphics window, **right-mouse-click** and select **Enter** to end the *Multiline* command.

- Next, we will create a line representing the location of a 2'-8" door.

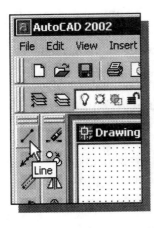

12. Select the **Line** command icon in the *Draw* toolbar. In the command prompt area, the message "*_line Specify first point:*" is displayed.

13. In the *Object Snap* toolbar, pick **Snap to Endpoint**. In the command prompt area, the message "*_endp of*" is displayed. AutoCAD now expects us to select a geometric entity on the screen.

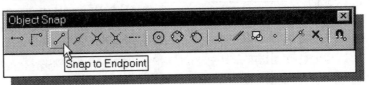

14. Pick the **top right corner** of the multiline we just created.

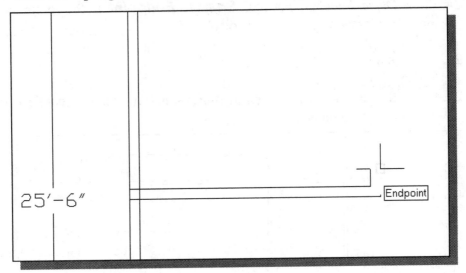

15. At the command prompt, enter **@0,2'8"** [**ENTER**].

16. Inside the graphics window, right-mouse-click and select **Enter** to end the *Line* command.

17. Select the **Multiline** command icon in the *Draw* toolbar. In the text window, the current settings "*Justification = Bottom, Scale = 1.00, Style = Wall*" are displayed. In the command prompt area, the message "*Specify start point or [Justification/Scale/Style]:*" is displayed.

18. Inside the graphics window, **right-mouse-click** to display the option menu.

19. Pick **Justification** in the option menu. In the command prompt area, the message "*Enter justification type [Top/Zero/Bottom] <Bottom>:*" is displayed.

20. Inside the graphics window, right-mouse-click to display the option menu and select **Top** so that the points we select will align to the top element.

21. In the *Object Snap* toolbar, pick **Snap From**. In the command prompt area, the message "*from Base point*" is displayed. AutoCAD now expects us to select a geometric entity on the screen.

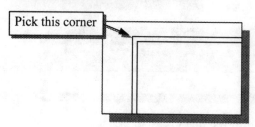

22. We will measure relative to the top left corner. Pick the corner as shown.

23. At the command prompt, enter **@10',0 [ENTER]**.

24. In the *Object Snap* toolbar, pick **Snap to Endpoint**. In the command prompt area, the message "*_endp of* " is displayed.

25. Pick the top endpoint of the reference line.

26. Inside the graphics window, **right-mouse-click** once and select **Enter** to end the *Multiline* command.

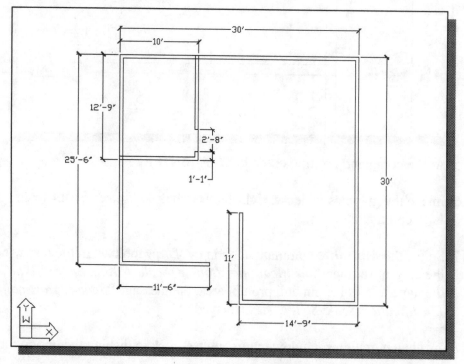

The main advantage of using a CAD system is the ability to create and remove geometric entities quickly and easily, using many of the available tools. Unlike traditional board drafting, where the draftsperson tends to create only the necessary entities on paper, CAD provides a much more flexible environment that requires a slightly different manner of thinking, as well as taking a different view of the tasks at hand.

Joining the walls using *Multiline Edit*

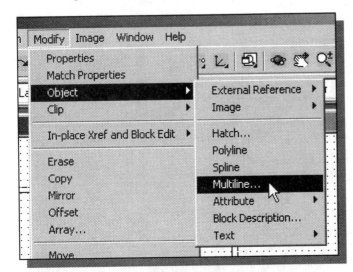

1. In the pull-down menus, select:

   [Modify] → **[Object]**
   → **[Multiline]**

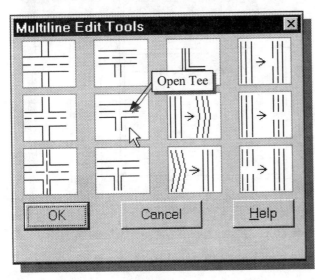

The *Multiline Edit Tools* dialog box appears. Select the **Help** button to see the description of the available *Multiline Edit Tools*.

2. Pick the ***Open Tee*** option in the dialog box.

3. Click **OK** to accept the selection of the *Open Tee* option.

➤ We will need to select two multilines for this option: first, select the multiline to trim or extend and, second, select the intersecting multiline.

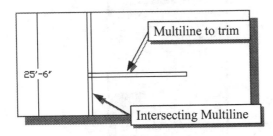

4. Pick the **horizontal multiline** as the *multiline to trim* as shown.

5. Pick the **vertical multiline** as the *intersecting multiline*.

6. Repeat the above steps and modify the connection of the other inside wall.

7. Inside the graphics window, **right-mouse-click** once and select **Enter** to end the *Mledit* command.

8. Using the *Multiline* options, create the additional walls and doorways as shown.

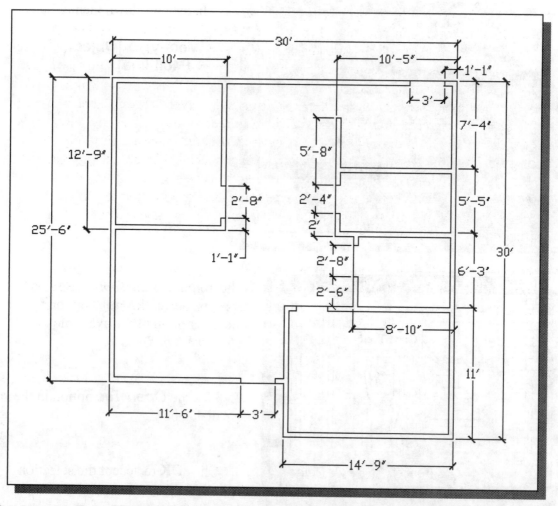

➤ Use the ***Trim/Extend***, ***Undo***, and ***Erase*** commands to assist the construction of the floor plan.

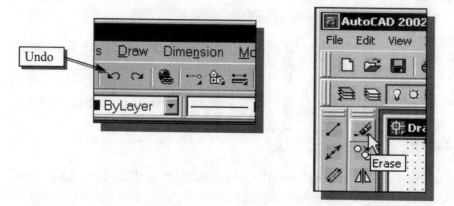

❖ Now is a good time to save the design. Select **[File]** → **[Save As]** in the pull-down menu and use ***FloorPlan*** as the *File name*.

Using *Layers* and Object Properties

In AutoCAD, **layers** can be thought of as transparent overlays on which we organize different kinds of design information. Typically, CAD entities that are created to describe one feature or function of a design are considered as related information and therefore can be organized into the same group. The objects we organized into the same group will usually have common properties such as colors, linetypes, and lineweights. Color helps us visually distinguish similar elements in our designs. Linetype helps us identify easily the different drafting elements, such as centerlines or hidden lines. Lineweight increases the legibility of an object through width. Consider the floor plan we are currently working on. The floor plan can be placed on one layer, electrical layout on another, and plumbing on a third layer. Organizing layers and the objects on layers makes it easier to manage the information in our designs. Layers can be used as a method to control the visibility of objects. We can temporarily switch *ON* or *OFF* any layer to help construction and editing of our designs.

AutoCAD allows us to create an infinite number of layers. In general, twenty to thirty layers are sufficient for most designs. Most companies also require designers and CAD operators to follow the company standards in organizing objects in layers.

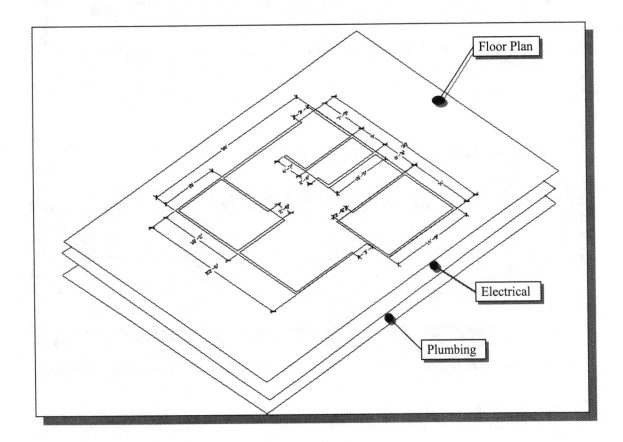

1. Pick **Layers** in the *Object Properties* toolbar.

❖ The *Layer Properties Manager* dialog box appears. AutoCAD creates a default layer, *layer 0*, which we cannot rename or delete. *Layer 0* has special properties used by the system.

❖ In AutoCAD, we always construct entities on a layer. It may be the default layer or a layer that we create. Each layer has associated properties such as the visibility setting, color, linetype, lineweight, and plot style.

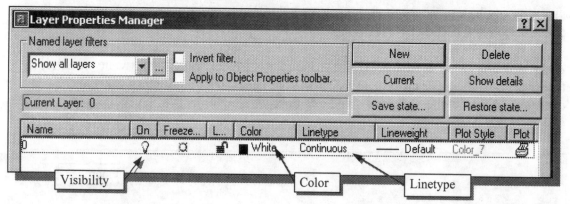

2. Click on the **NEW** button. Notice a layer is automatically added to the list of layers.

3. AutoCAD will assign a generic name to the new layer (*Layer1*). Enter **BathRoom** as the name of the new layer.

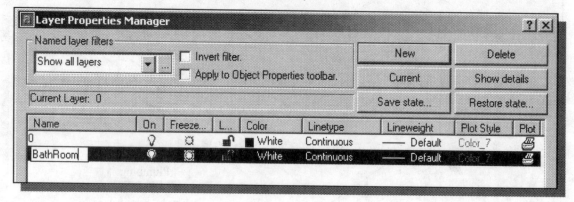

❖ Layer properties can be adjusted by clicking on the icon or name of a property. For example, clicking on the *light-bulb* icon will toggle the visibility of the layer *ON* or *OFF*.

4. Pick the color swatch or the color name (*White*) of the *BathRoom* layer. The *Select Color* dialog box appears.

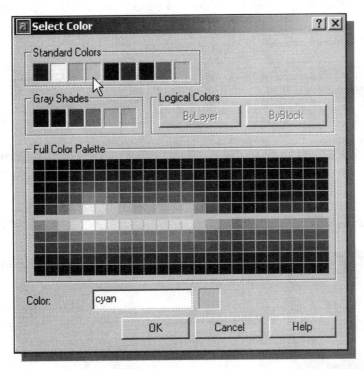

5. Pick **Cyan** in the *Standard Colors* section. Notice the current color setting is displayed at the bottom of the dialog box.

6. Click on the **OK** button to accept the color assignment.

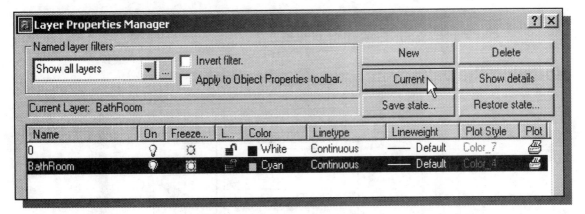

7. Click on the **Current** button to make *BathRoom* the *Current Layer*. There can only be one *Current Layer*, and new entities are automatically placed on the layer that is set to be the *Current Layer*.

8. Click on the **OK** button to accept the settings and exit the *Layer Properties Manager* dialog box.

❖ The *Object Properties* toolbar near the top of the AutoCAD screen shows the status of object properties. There are two strategies for assigning *colors, linetypes*, and *lineweights* in AutoCAD: assign to individual objects, or assign **ByLayer** properties. Using the *ByLayer* method is the preferred method, since it allows us to modify all related objects quickly and easily.

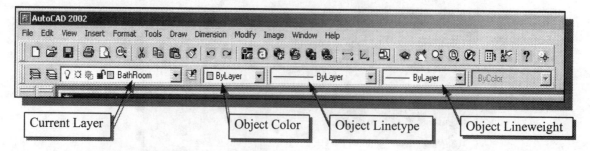

Using *Zoom Realtime*

1. Click on the **Zoom Realtime** icon in the *Standard* toolbar area.

2. Move the cursor near the center of the graphics window.

3. Inside the graphics window, **push and hold down the left-mouse-button**, then move upward to enlarge the current display scale factor. (Press the **[Esc]** key to exit the *Zoom* command.)

4. Use the **Pan Realtime** option to reposition the display so that we can work on the bathroom of the floor plan.

Modeling the bathroom

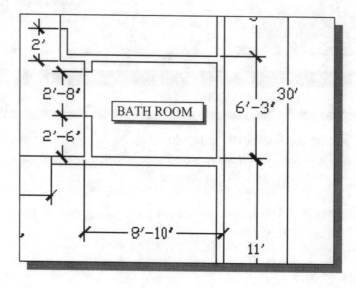

1. In the *Status Bar* area, reset the option buttons so that only the *MODEL* button is switched *ON*.

2. Click on the **Rectangle** command icon in the *Draw* toolbar. In the command prompt area, the message "*Specify first corner point:*" is displayed.

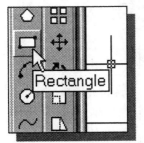

3. In the *Object Snap* toolbar, pick **Snap to Endpoint**. In the command prompt area, the message "*_endp of*" is displayed. AutoCAD now expects us to select a geometric entity on the screen.

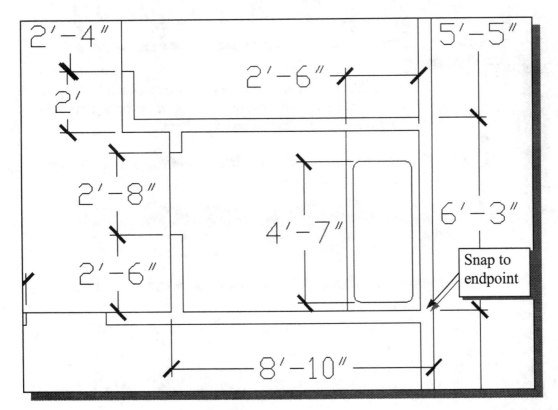

4. Use the *relative coordinate entry method* and create the outer rectangle of the tub.

5. Complete the inner shape by creating a rectangle with a distance of 3" from the outer rectangle and rounded corners of 3" radius.

6. Create two rectangles (*10" X 20"* and *20" X 30"*) with rounded corners (Radius 3") and position them as shown. Use the *Explode* command to change the rectangle into lines prior to creating the fillets.

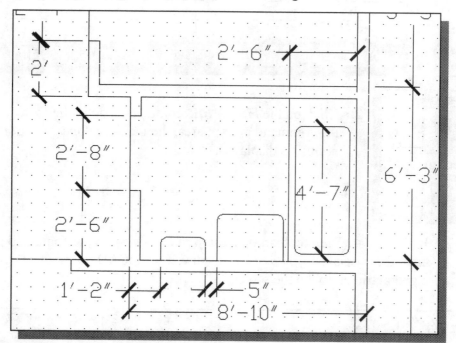

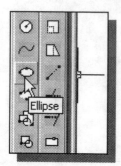

7. Select the **Ellipse** command icon in the *Draw* toolbar. In the command prompt area, the message "*Specify axis endpoint of ellipse or [Arc/Center]:*" is displayed.

8. In the *Object Snap* toolbar, pick **Snap to Midpoint**. In the command prompt area, the message "*_mid of*" is displayed.

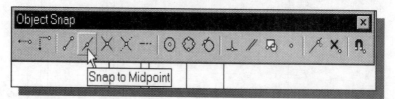

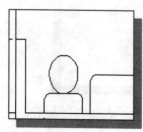

9. Pick the top horizontal line of the small rectangle we just created.

10. For the second point location, enter **@0,20"** [**ENTER**].

11. For the third point, enter **@7.5",0** [**ENTER**].

❖ An ellipse has a major axis, the longest distance between two points on the ellipse, and a minor axis, the shorter distance across the ellipse. The three points we specified identify the two axes.

Controlling *Layer Visibility*

AutoCAD does not display or plot the objects that are on invisible layers. To make layers invisible, we can *freeze* or *turn off* those layers. Turning off layers only temporarily removes the objects from the screen; the objects remain active in the CAD database. Freezing layers will make the objects invisible and also disable the objects in the CAD database. Freezing layers will improve object selection performance and reduce regeneration time for complex designs. When we *thaw* a frozen layer, AutoCAD updates the CAD database with the screen coordinates for all objects in the design.

1. On the *Object Properties* toolbar, choose the *Layer Control* box with the left-mouse-button.

2. Move the cursor over the light-bulb icon for *layer 0*. The tool tip "*Turn a layer On or Off*" appears.

3. **Left-mouse-click once** and notice the icon color is changed to a dark color, representing the layer (*layer 0*) is turned *OFF*.

4. Move the cursor into the graphics window and **left-mouse-click once** to accept the layer control settings.

➢ On your own, practice turning on *layer 0* and freezing/thawing *layer 0*. What would happen if we turn off all layers?

Adding a New Layer

1. Pick **Layers** in the *Object Properties* toolbar. The *Layer Properties Manager* dialog box appears.

2. Create a new layer (layer name: **Walls**) and change the layer color to **Green**.

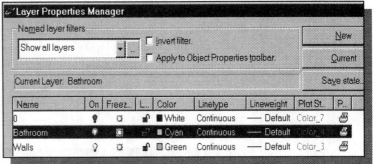

Name	On	Freez.	L.	Color	Linetype	Lineweight	Plot St.	P.
0	♀	✿	♂	■ White	Continuous	—— Default	Color_7	🖨
Bathroom	♀	✿	♂	■ Cyan	Continuous	—— Default	Color_4	🖨
Walls	♀	✿	♂	▣ Green	Continuous	—— Default	Color_3	🖨

3. Turn *OFF* the *BathRoom* layer and set the **Walls** layer as the *Current Layer*.

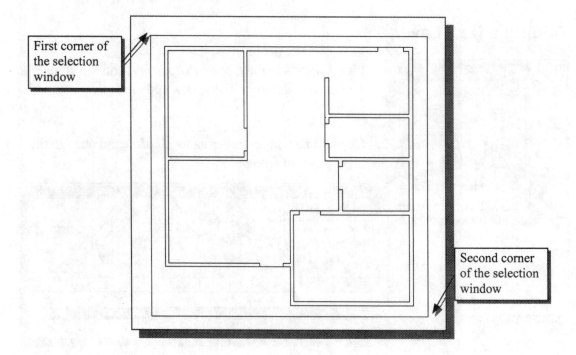

Name	**On**	**Freeze...**	**L...**	**Color**	**Linetype**	**Lineweight**	**Plot Style**	**Plot**
0	♀	¤	⌐	■ White	Continuous	—— Default	Color_7	
BathRoom	♀	¤	⌐	□ Cyan	Continuous	—— Default	Color_4	
Walls	♀	¤		■ Green	Continuous	—— Default	Color_3	

4. Click on the **OK** button to accept the settings.

Moving objects to a different layer

❖ **AutoCAD® 2002** provides a flexible graphical user interface that allows users to select graphical entities BEFORE the command is selected (*Pre-selection*), or AFTER the command is selected (*Post-selection*). The procedure we have used so far is the *post-selection* option. We can pre-select one or more objects by clicking on the objects at the command prompt (**Command:**). To deselect the selected items, press the [**Esc**] key twice.

1. Inside the graphics window, pre-select all objects by enclosing all objects inside a **selection window** as shown.

First corner of the selection window

Second corner of the selection window

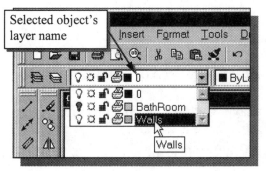

2. On the *Object Properties* toolbar, choose the **Layer Control** box with the left-mouse-button.

   Notice the layer name displayed in the *Layer Control* box is the selected object's assigned layer and layer properties.

3. In the *Layer Control* box, click on the *Walls* layer name.

4. Make *Walls* invisible by turning the layer *OFF*.

➢ On your own, experiment with turning layers on or off and moving objects from one layer to another.

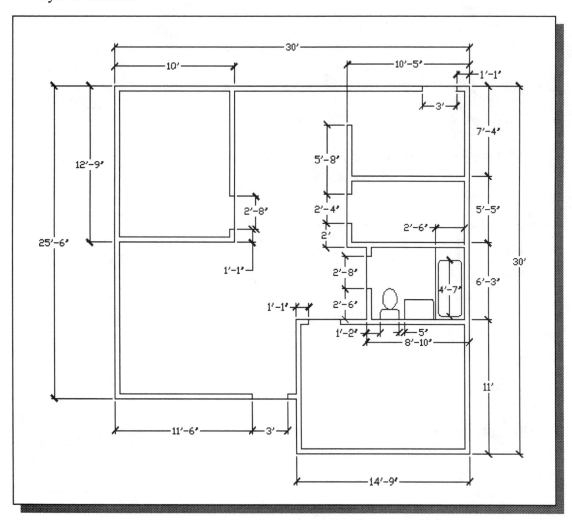

Questions:

1. Describe some of the advantages of using *layers*.

2. List two methods to control the *layer visibility* in **AutoCAD® 2002**.

3. What is the difference between *freezing* a layer and *turning off* a layer?

4. When and why would you use the *Multiline* command?

5. Identify the following commands:

(a)

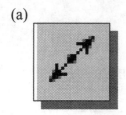

(b)

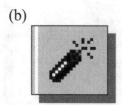

(c)

(d)

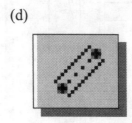

Exercises:

1. **D**imensions are in inches.

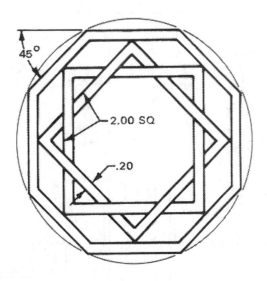

2. Wall thickness: 5 inch

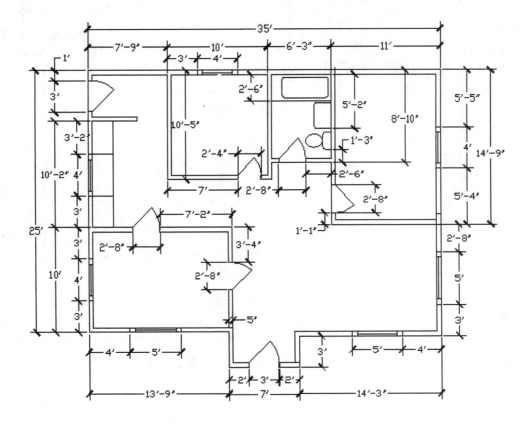

3.   Wall thickness: 5 inch

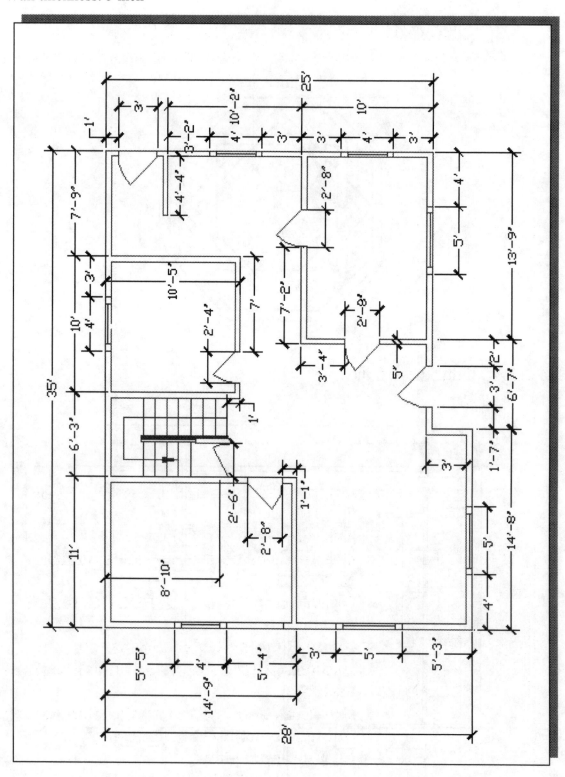

Lesson 5
Orthographic Views in Multiview Drawings

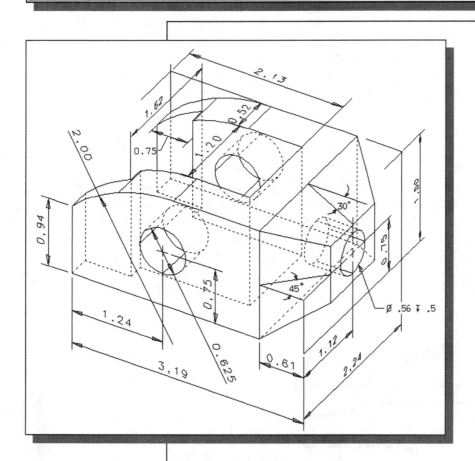

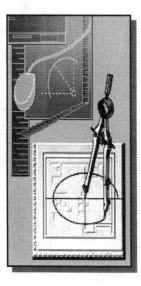

Learning Objectives

♦ **Create 2D orthographic views using AutoCAD.**

♦ **Draw, using the CONSTRUCTION LINE command.**

♦ **Using Running Object Snaps.**

♦ **Use AutoCAD's *AutoSnap* and *AutoTrack* features.**

♦ **Create a Miter line to transfer dimensions.**

♦ **Using Projection lines between orthographic views.**

♦ **Use the POLAR Tracking option.**

Introduction

Most drawings produced and used in industry are ***multiview drawings***. Multiview drawings are used to provide accurate three-dimensional object information on two-dimensional media, a means of communicating all of the information necessary to transform an idea or concept into reality. The standards and conventions of multiview drawings have been developed over many years, which equip us with a universally understood method of communication. The age of computers has greatly altered the design process, and several CAD methods are now available to help generate multiview drawings using CAD systems.

Multiview drawings usually require several orthographic views to define the shape of a three-dimensional object. Each orthographic view is a two-dimensional drawing showing only two of the three dimensions of the three-dimensional object. Consequently, no individual view contains sufficient information to completely define the shape of the three-dimensional object. We must look at all orthographic views together to comprehend the shape of the three-dimensional object. The arrangement and relationship between the views are therefore very important in multiview drawings. In this lesson, we will look at the more common methods of creating two-dimensional orthographic views with AutoCAD.

The *LOCATOR* Design

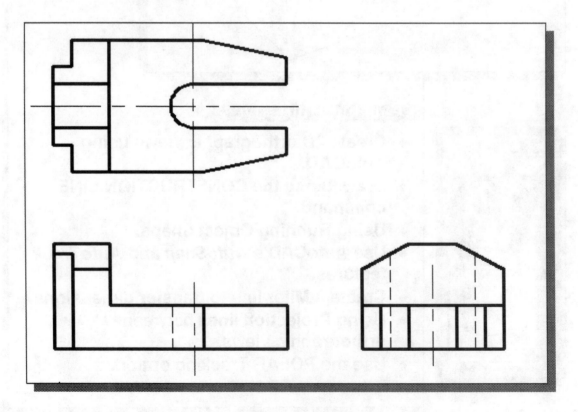

Starting Up AutoCAD® 2002

1. Select the **AutoCAD 2002** option on the *Program* menu or select the **AutoCAD 2002** icon on the *Desktop*.

2. In the *AutoCAD Today* startup dialog box, select the **Create Drawings** tab with the single click of the left-mouse-button.

3. In the startup dialog box, select the **Start from Scratch** option with a single click of the left-mouse-button.

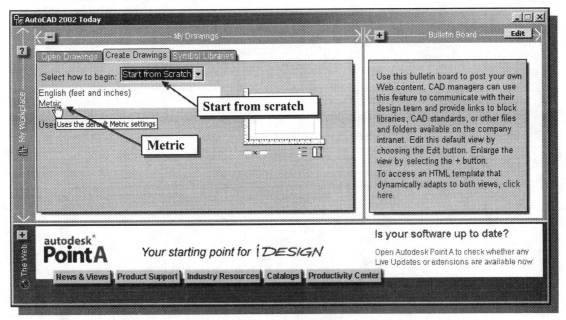

4. In the *Default Settings* section, pick **Metric** as the drawing units.

- We have two drawing windows opened in the AutoCAD screen window. Note that the units setting of *Drawing1* is set to the default system units. The *Drawing2* window is set up through the AutoCAD *Quick Setup* wizard, which sets the units to the metric system. To avoid any confusion in following through the tutorial, we will close the *Drawing1* window.

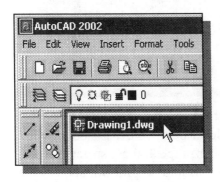

5. Switch to the *Drawing1* window by left-clicking once in the title area of the window.

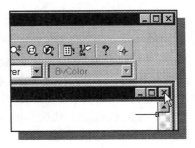

6. Close the window by clicking the **Close** icon located at the upper-right-corner of the *Drawing1* window.

GRID and *SNAP* intervals Setup

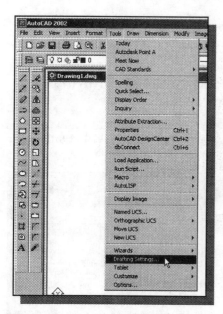

1. In the pull-down menus, select:
   [Tools] → [Drafting Settings]

2. In the *Drafting Settings* dialog box, select the **SNAP and GRID** tab if it is not the page on top.

3. Change *Grid Spacing* to **10** for both X and Y directions.

4. Also adjust the *Snap Spacing* to **10** for both X and Y directions.

5. Pick **OK** to exit the *Drafting Settings* dialog box.

The *Locator* part

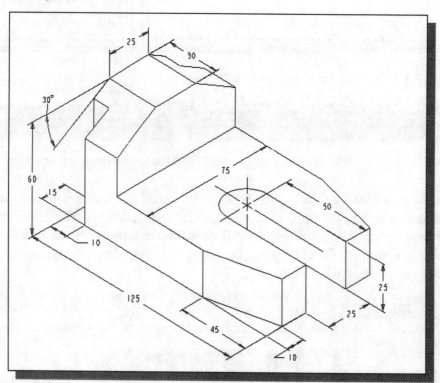

➤ Before going through the tutorial, make a rough sketch of a multiview drawing of the part. How many 2D views will be necessary to fully describe the part? Based on your knowledge of **AutoCAD® 2002** so far, how would you arrange and construct these 2D views? Take a few minutes to consider these questions and do preliminary planning by sketching on a piece of paper. You are also encouraged to construct the orthographic views on your own prior to following through the tutorial.

Layers setup

1. Pick **Layers** in the *Object Properties* toolbar.

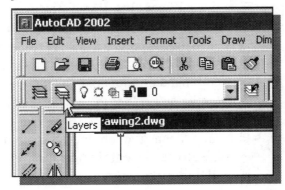

2. Click on the **New** icon to create new layers.

3. Create **two new layers** with the following settings:

Layer	Color	LineType
Construction	White	Continuous
Object	Yellow	Continuous

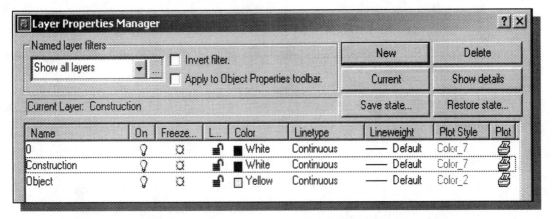

4. Highlight the layer **Construction** in the list of layers.

5. Click on the **Current** button to set layer **Construction** as the *Current Layer*.

6. Click on the **OK** button to accept the settings and exit the *Layer Properties Manager* dialog box.

7. In the *Status Bar* area, reset the option buttons so that only *SNAP, GRID*, and *MODEL* are switched **ON**.

Drawing *Construction Lines*

❖ Construction lines are lines that extend to infinity. Construction lines are usually used as references for creating other objects. We will also place the construction lines on the *Construction* layer so that the layer can later be frozen or turned off.

1. Select the **Construction Line** icon in the *Draw* toolbar. In the command prompt area, the message "*_xline Specify a point or [Hor/Ver/Ang/Bisect/Offset]:*" is displayed.

   • To orient construction lines, we generally specify two points. Note that other orientation options are also available.

2. Select a location near the lower-left corner of the graphics window. It is not necessary to align objects to the world coordinate origin. CAD systems provide us with many powerful tools to manipulate geometry. Our main goal is to use the CAD systems as a flexible and powerful tool, and to be very efficient and effective with the systems.

3. Pick a location above the last point to create a **vertical line**.

4. Move the cursor toward the right of the first point and pick a location to create a **horizontal line**.

5. Inside the graphics window, **right-mouse-click** to end the *Construction Line* command.

6. In the *Status Bar* area, turn **OFF** the *SNAP* option.

Using the *Offset* command

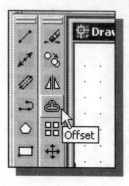

1. Select the **Offset** icon in the *Modify* toolbar. In the command prompt area, the message "*Specify offset distance or [Through]:*" is displayed.

2. In the command prompt area, enter: **125 [ENTER]**.

3. In the command prompt area, the message "*Select object to offset or <exit>:*" is displayed. Pick the **vertical line** on the screen.

4. AutoCAD next asks us to identify the direction of the offset. Pick a location that is to the **right** of the vertical line.

5. Inside the graphics window, **right-mouse-click** to end the *Offset* command.

6. Hit the [**SPACE BAR**], or right-mouse-click inside the graphics window and select **Repeat Offset** in the popup list, to repeat the *Offset* command.

7. In the command prompt area, enter: **60 [ENTER]**.

8. In the command prompt area, the message "*Select object to offset or <exit>:*" is displayed. Pick the **horizontal line** on the screen.

9. AutoCAD next asks us to identify the direction of the offset. Pick a location that is **above** the horizontal line.

10. Inside the graphics window, **right-mouse-click** to end the *Offset* command.

11. Repeat the *Offset* command and create the lines as shown.

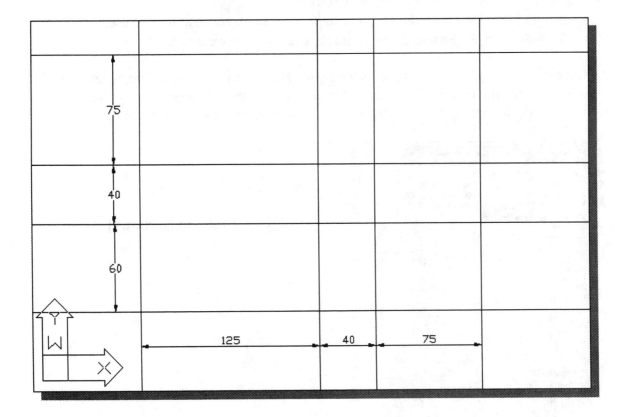

Set layer *Object* as the current layer

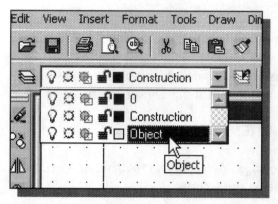

1. On the *Object Properties* toolbar, choose the **Layer Control** box with the left-mouse-button.

2. Move the cursor over the name of the layer **Object**. The tool tip "*Object*" appears.

3. **Left-mouse-click once** and the layer *Object* is set as the *Current Layer*.

Using the *Running Object Snaps*

In **AutoCAD® 2002**, while using geometry construction commands, we can snap the cursor to points on objects such as endpoints, midpoints, centers, and intersections. In AutoCAD, this tool is called the ***Object Snap***.

We can turn on object snaps in one of two ways:
- **Single Point (or override) Object Snaps**: Sets an object snap for one use.
- **Running Object Snaps**: Sets object snaps *active* until we turn them off.

The procedure we have used so far is the *Single Point Object Snaps* option, where we select the specific object snap from the *Object Snap* toolbar for one use only. We will next demonstrate using the *Running Object Snaps* to assist our construction.

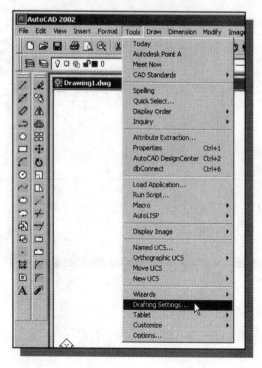

1. In the pull-down menus, select:

   [Tools] → [Drafting Settings]

2. In the *Drafting Settings* dialog box select the **OBJECT SNAP** tab.

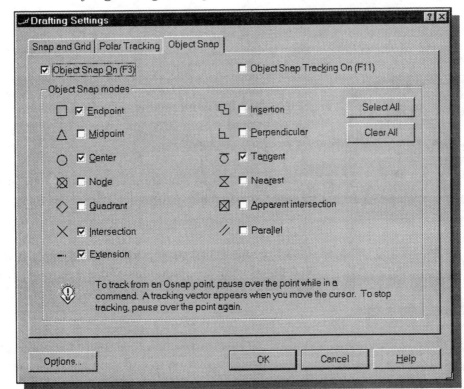

The *Running Object Snap* options can be turned on or off by clicking the different options listed. Notice the different symbols for the different *Object Snap* options, especially the intersection option.

3. Turn *ON* the *Running Object Snap* by clicking the **Object Snap On** box, or hit the **[F3]** key once.

4. Confirm the *Intersection, Endpoint* and *Extension* options are switched *ON* and click on the **OK** button to accept the settings and exit from the *Drafting Settings* dialog box.

❖ Notice in the *Status Bar* area the *OSNAP* button is switched *ON*. We can toggle the *Running Object Snap* option on or off by clicking the *OSNAP* button.

5. Press the **[F3]** key once and notice the *OSNAP* button is switched *OFF* in the *Status Bar* area.

6. Press the **[F3]** key again and notice the *OSNAP* button is now switched *ON* in the *Status Bar* area.

➤ **AutoCAD® 2002** provides many input methods and shortcuts; you are encouraged to examine the different options and choose the option that best fits your own style.

Creating *Object Lines*

We will define the areas for the front-view, top-view and side-view by adding object lines using the *Running Object Snap* option.

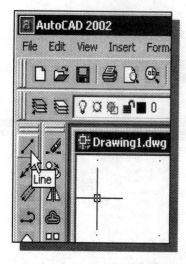

1. Select the **Line** command icon in the *Draw* toolbar. In the command prompt area, the message "*_line Specify first point:*" is displayed.

2. Move the cursor to the intersection of any two lines and notice the visual aid automatically displayed at the intersection.

3. Pick the four intersection points closest to the lower left corner to create the four sides of the area of the front view.

4. Inside the graphics window, **right-mouse-click** to activate the option menu and select **Enter** with the left-mouse-button to end the *Line* command.

5. Repeat the *Line* command to define the top-view and side-view as shown.

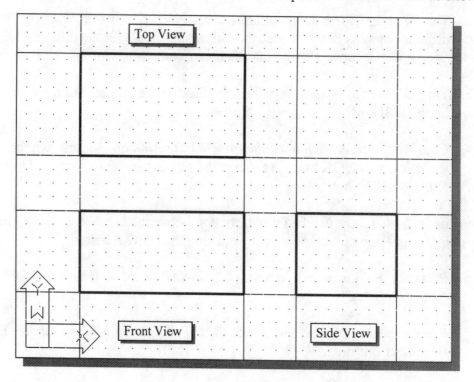

Turn *OFF* the Construction Lines layer

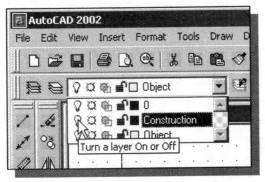

1. On the *Object Properties* toolbar, choose the **Layer Control** box with the left-mouse-button.

2. Move the cursor over the light-bulb icon for layer **Construction**. The tool tip "*Turn a layer On or Off*" appears.

3. **Left-mouse-click once** and notice the icon color is changed to gray, representing the layer (layer *Construction*) is turned *OFF*.

Adding more objects in the Front View

1. Use the **Offset** command and create the two parallel lines in the front view as shown.

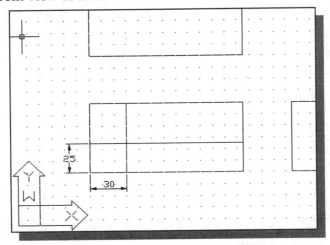

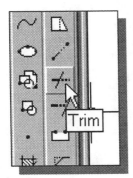

2. Use the **Trim** command and modify the front view as shown.

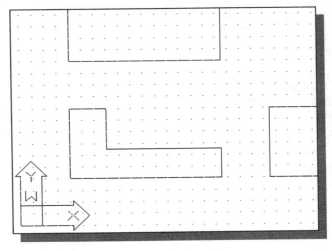

AutoCAD's *AutoSnap*™ and *AutoTrack*™ features

AutoCAD's *AutoSnap* and *AutoTrack* provide visual aids when we are using *Object Snap*. The main advantages of *AutoSnap* and *AutoTrack* are as follows:

- **Symbols**: Automatically displays the *Object Snap* type at the object snap location.

- **Tooltips**: Automatically displays the *Object Snap* type below the cursor.

- **Magnet**: Locks the cursor onto a snap point when the cursor is near the point.

With **Object Snap Tracking,** the cursor can track along alignment paths based on other object snap points when specifying points in a command. To use *Object Snap Tracking*, one or more object snaps must be switched on. The basic rules of using the **Object Snap Tracking** option are as follows:

- To track from a *Running Object Snap* point, pause over the point while in a command.
- A tracking vector appears when we move the cursor.
- To stop tracking, pause over the point again.
- When multiple *Running Object Snaps* are on, press the **[TAB]** key to cycle through available snap points when the object snap aperture box is on an object.

1. In the *Status Bar* area, turn *ON* the *OTRACK* option.

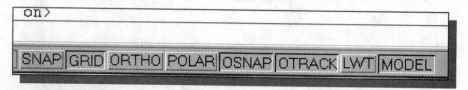

2. Select the **Line** command icon in the *Draw* toolbar. In the command prompt area, the message "_line *Specify first point:*" is displayed.

3. Move the cursor near the top right corner of the vertical protrusion in the front view. Notice that *AutoSnap* automatically locks the cursor to the corner and displays the **Endpoint** symbol.

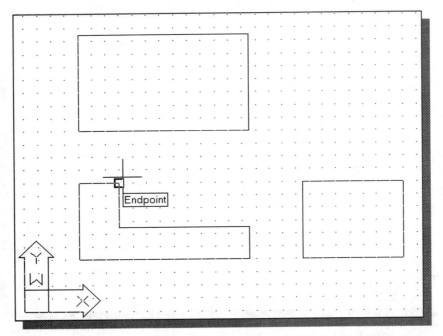

4. Move the cursor upward and notice that *Object Tracking* displays a dashed line, showing the alignment to the top right corner of the vertical protrusion in the front view. Move the cursor near the top horizontal line of the top view and notice that *AutoSnap* displays the intersection point.

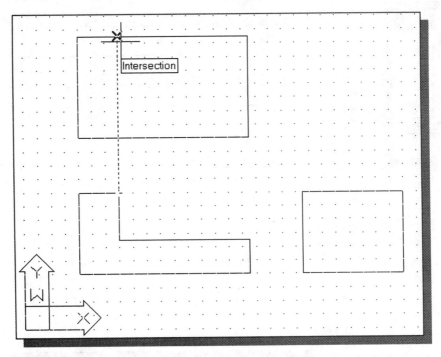

5. Left-mouse-click to place the starting point of a line at the intersection.

6. Move the cursor to the top-left corner of the front view to activate the tracking feature.

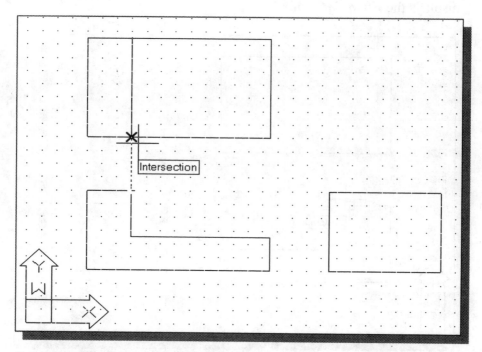

7. Create the line as shown in the above figure.

Adding more objects in the Top View

1. Use the **Offset** command and create the two parallel lines in the top-view as shown.

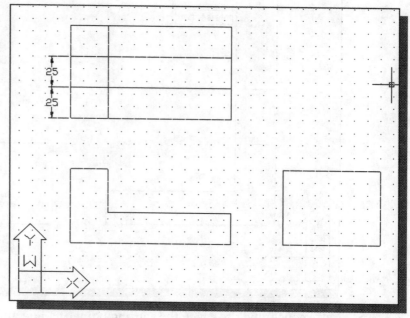

2. Move the cursor to the *Standard* toolbar area and **right-mouse-click** on any icon to display a list of toolbar menu groups.

3. Select **Object Snap**, with the left-mouse-button, to display the *Object Snap* toolbar on the screen.

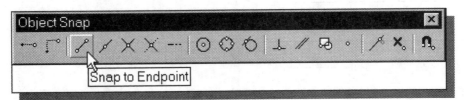

4. Select the **Line** command icon in the *Draw* toolbar. In the command prompt area, the message "*_line Specify first point:*" is displayed.

5. In the *Object Snap* toolbar, pick **Snap From**. In the command prompt area, the message "*_from Base point*" is displayed. AutoCAD now expects us to select a geometric entity on the screen.

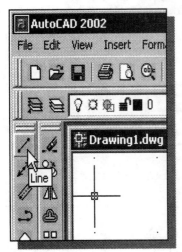

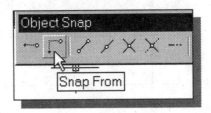

> The **Single Point (or override) Object Snap** overrides the **Running Object Snap** option.

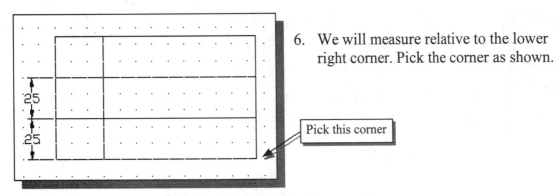

6. We will measure relative to the lower right corner. Pick the corner as shown.

Pick this corner

7. In the command prompt area, enter **@0,10 [ENTER]**.

8. In the *Object Snap* toolbar, pick **Snap From.** Pick the lower-right corner of the top view again.

9. In the command prompt area, enter **@-45,0 [ENTER]**.

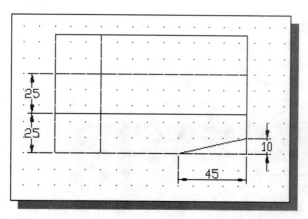

10. Inside the graphics window, **right-mouse-click** to activate the option menu and select **Enter** with the left-mouse-button to end the *Line* command.

11. Repeat the procedure and create the line and circle (diameter 25mm) as shown in the below figure.

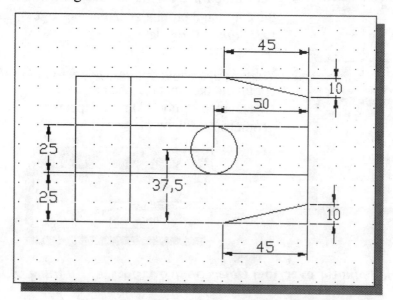

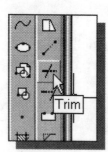

12. Select the **Trim** icon in the *Modify* toolbar. In the command prompt area, the message "*Select boundary edges... Select objects:*" is displayed.

13. Pick the following objects as boundary edges: the circle, and the lines that are near the circle.

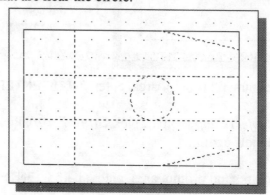

14. Inside the graphics window, **right-mouse-click** to accept the selected objects.

15. Select the unwanted portions and modify the objects as shown.

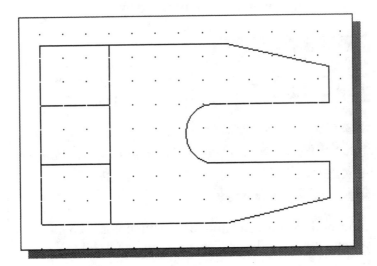

16. On your own, use the **Offset** and **Trim** commands and modify the top view as shown.

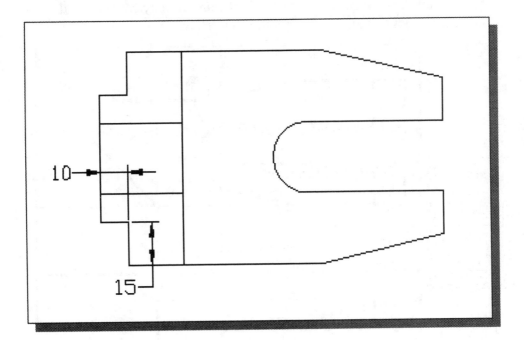

Drawing the *Miter Line*

The *45° miter line* method is a simple and straightforward procedure to transfer measurements in between the top view and the side view.

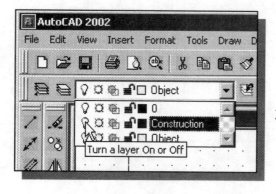

1. On the *Object Properties* toolbar, choose the **Layer Control** box with the left-mouse-button.

2. Move the cursor over the light-bulb icon for layer *Construction*. The tool tip *"Turn a layer On or Off"* appears.

3. **Left-mouse-click once** and notice the icon color is changed to a light color, representing the layer (layer *Construction*) is turned *ON*.

4. **Left-mouse-click once** over the name of the layer **Construction** to set it as the *Current Layer*.

5. Use the **Line** command and create the *miter line* by connecting the two intersections of the construction lines as shown.

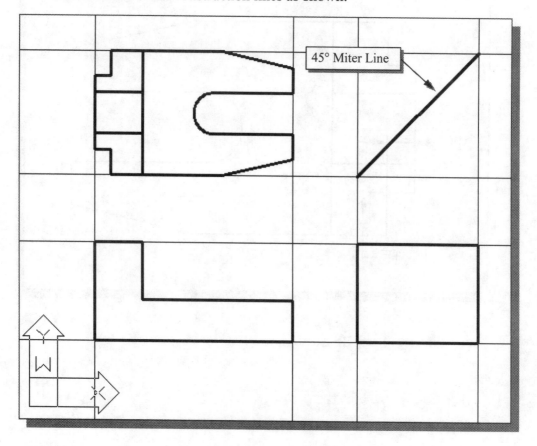

45° Miter Line

6. Use the **Construction Line** command and create horizontal projection lines (right-mouse-click and select the **Horizontal** option) through all the corners in the top view as shown.

7. Use the **Trim** command and trim the projection lines as shown.

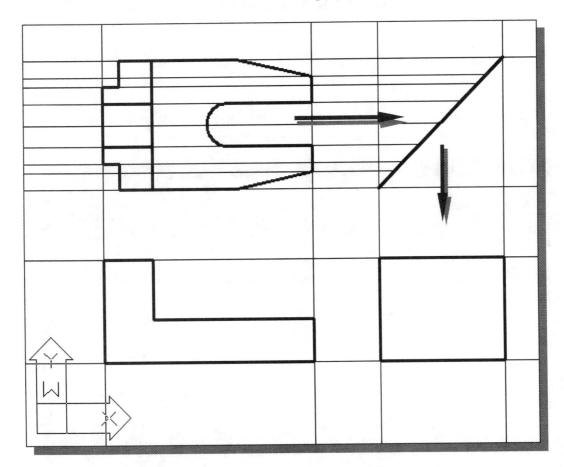

8. Add **Construction Lines** (vertical option) through all the intersection points that are on the *miter line*.

More Layers setup

1. Pick **Layers** in the *Object Properties* toolbar.

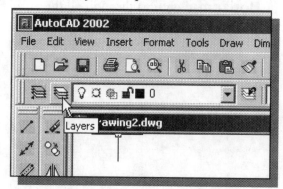

2. Click on the **New** icon to create new layers.

3. Create two **new layers** with the following settings:

Layer	Color	LineType
Hidden	Cyan	HIDDEN
Center	Red	CENTER

- The default linetype is *Continuous.* To use other linetypes, click on the **Load** button in the *Select Linetype* dialog box and select the desired linetypes.

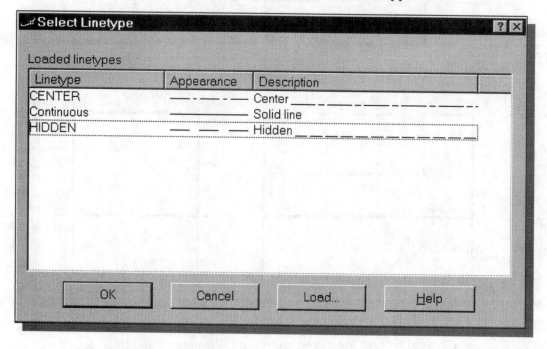

4. On your own, set the layer **Object** as the *Current Layer.*

Top View to Side View Projection

1. Using the *Running Object Snaps*, create the necessary **object-lines** in the side view.

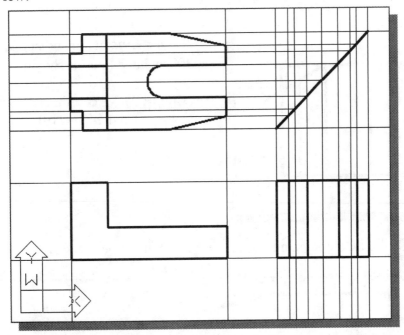

2. Set layer **Hidden** as the *Current Layer* and create the two necessary hidden lines in the side view.

3. Set layer **Center** as the *Current Layer* and create the necessary centerlines in the side view.

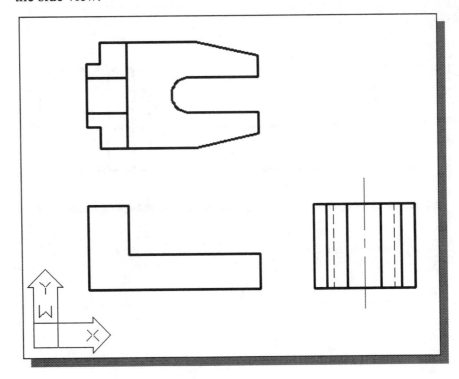

4. In the *Layer Control* box, turn **OFF** the construction lines.

5. Set layer **Object** as the *Current Layer*.

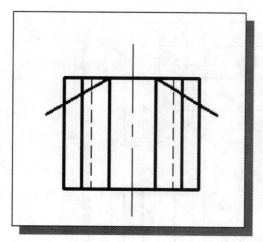

6. Use the **Line** command and create the two 30° inclined lines as shown.

    (Hint: Relative coordinate entries of @40<-30 and @40<210)

7. Use the *Line* command and create a horizontal line in the side view as shown.

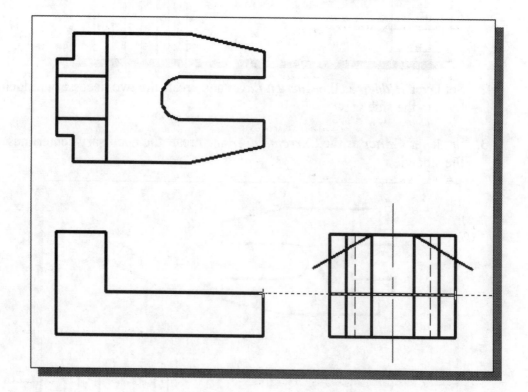

8. On your own, use the **Trim** command and remove the unwanted portions in the side view.

Completing the Front View

1. Select the **Line** command icon in the *Draw* toolbar. In the command prompt area, the message "*_line Specify first point:*" is displayed.

2. Move the cursor to the top-left corner in the side view and the bottom-left corner in the top view to activate the *Object Tracking* option to both corners.

3. Left-mouse-click once when the cursor is aligned to both corners as shown.

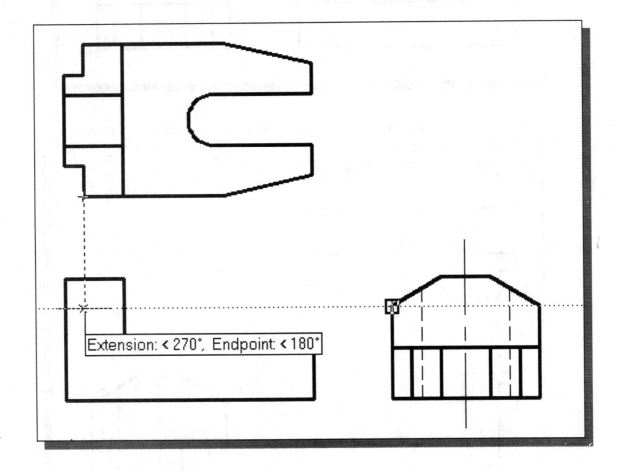

4. Create the **horizontal line** as shown.

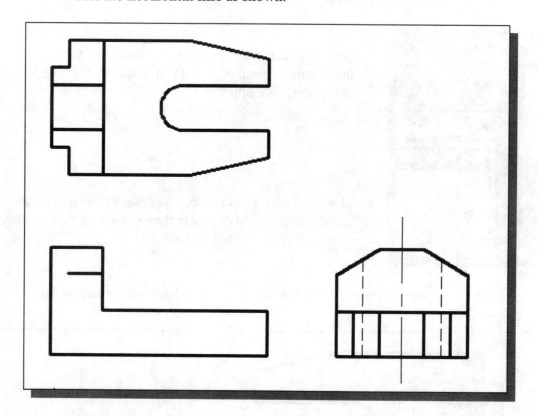

5. Repeat the procedure and create the lines in the front view as shown.

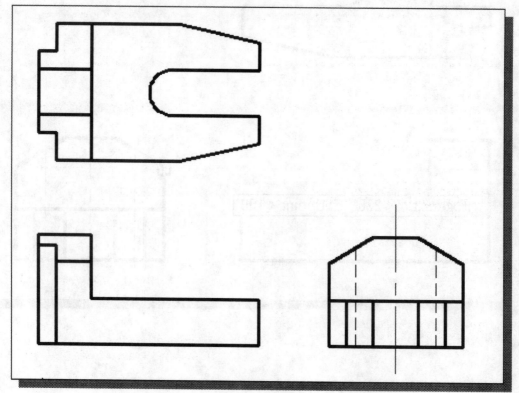

6. Add in any additional object lines that are necessary.

7. Set layer **Hidden** as the *Current Layer* and create the necessary hidden lines in the front view.

8. Set layer **Center** as the *Current Layer* and create the necessary centerlines in the top view and front view.

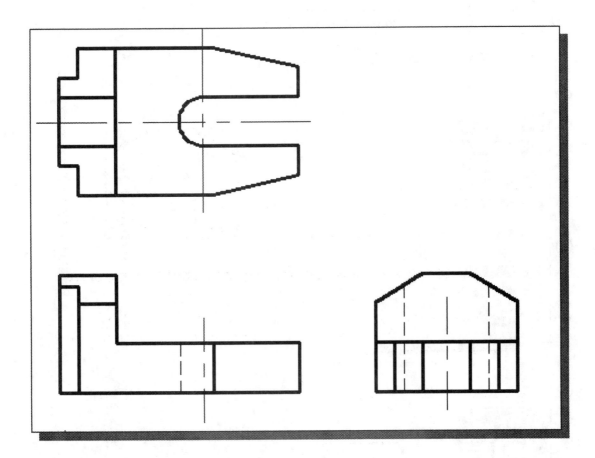

Saving the CAD file

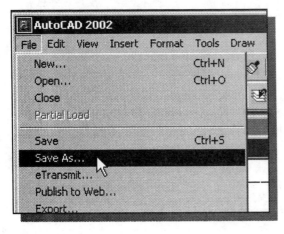

1. In the pull-down menus, select:

    [File] → [Save As]

2. In the *Save Drawing As* dialog box, select the folder you want to store the CAD file and enter **Locator** in the *File name* box.

3. Pick **Save** in the *Save Drawing As* dialog box to accept the selections and save the file.

Questions:

1. Explain what an orthographic view is and why it is important to engineering graphics.

2. What does the *Running Object Snaps* option allow us to do?

3. Explain how a *miter line* can assist us in creating orthographic views.

4. Describe the AutoCAD *AutoSnap* and *AutoTrack* options.

5. Identify the following commands:

(a)

(b)

(c)

(d)

Exercises: (Unless otherwise specified, dimensions are in inches.)

1.

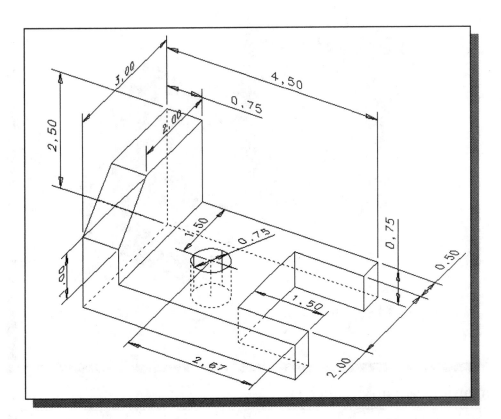

2.

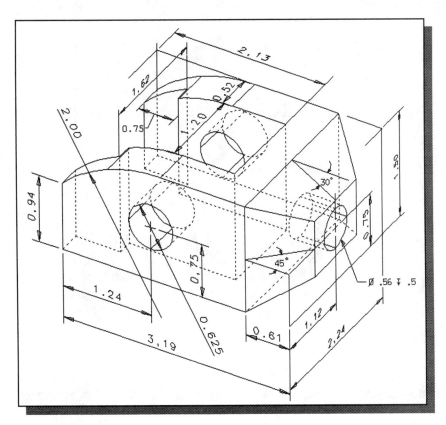

3.

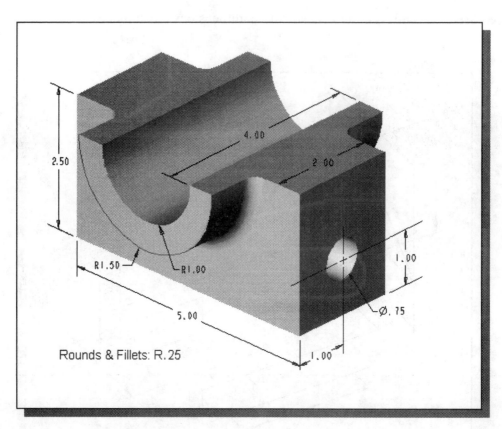

Rounds & Fillets: R.25

4. Dimensions are in Millimeters.

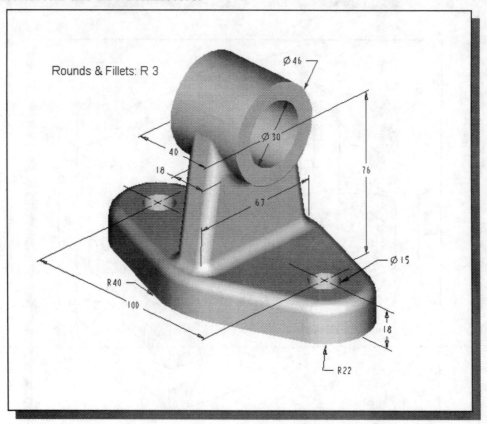

5.

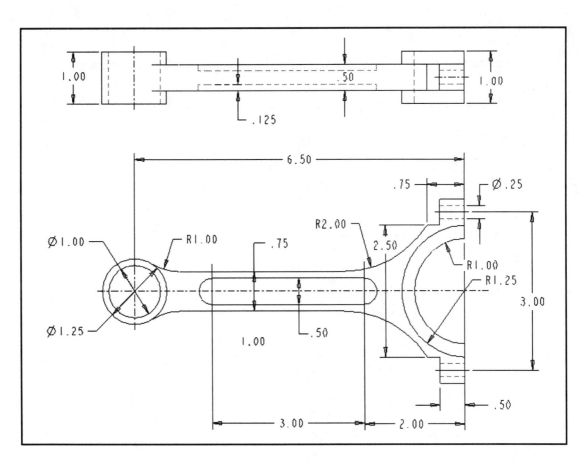

NOTES:

Lesson 6
Basic Dimensioning and Notes

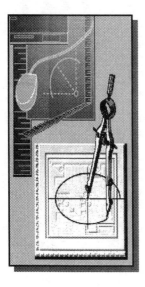

Learning Objectives

♦ **Understand Dimensioning Nomenclature and Basics.**

♦ **Display and use the Dimension toolbar.**

♦ **Use the AutoCAD Dimension Style Manager.**

♦ **Create Center Marks.**

♦ **Add Linear and Angular Dimensions.**

♦ **Use the SINGLE LINE TEXT command.**

♦ **Create Special Characters in Notes.**

Introduction

In order to manufacture a finalized design, the complete *shape* and *size* description must be shown on the drawings of the design. Thus far, we have illustrated how to use **AutoCAD® 2002** to define the *shape* of designs. In this lesson, we will discuss the procedures to convey the *size* definitions of designs using **AutoCAD® 2002**. The *tools of size description* are known as *dimensions* and *notes*.

Considerable experience and judgement is required for accurate size description. Detail drawings should contain only those dimensions that are necessary to make the design. Dimensions for the same feature of the design should be given only once in the same drawing. Nothing should be left to chance or guesswork on a drawing. Drawings should be dimensioned to avoid any possibility of questions. Dimensions should be carefully positioned; preferably near the profile of the feature being dimensioned. The designer and the CAD operator should be as familiar as possible with materials, methods of manufacturing, and shop processes.

Traditionally, detailing a drawing is the biggest bottleneck of the design process; and when doing board drafting, dimensioning is one of the most time consuming and tedious tasks. Today, most CAD systems provide what is known as an **auto-dimensioning feature**, where the CAD system automatically creates the extension lines, dimensional lines, arrowheads, and dimension values. Most CAD systems also provide an **associative dimensioning feature** so that the system automatically updates the dimensions when the drawing is modified.

The *BRACKET* Design

Starting Up AutoCAD 2002

1. Select the **AutoCAD 2002** option on the *Program* menu or select the **AutoCAD 2002** icon on the *Desktop*.
2. Confirm the startup option is set to **Start from Scratch**, as shown in the figure below.

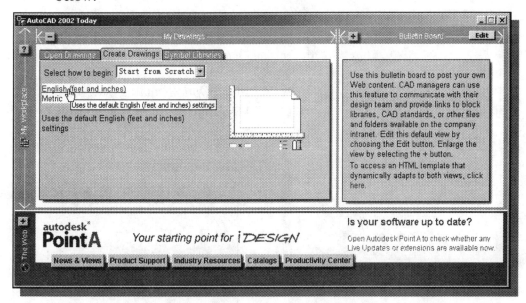

3. In the *Default Settings* section, pick **English (feet and inches)** as the drawing units.

4. Pick **OK** in the *AutoCAD Today* startup dialog box to accept the selected settings.

- We have two drawing windows opened in the AutoCAD screen window. Note that the units setting of *Drawing1* is set to either the default English units system or the default Metric units. The *Drawing2* window is set up through the AutoCAD *Quick Setup* wizard, which set the units to the English units system. To avoid any confusion in following through the tutorial, we will close the *Drawing1* window.

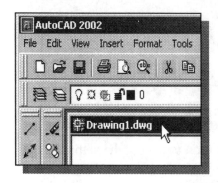

5. Switch to the *Drawing1* window by left-clicking once in the title area of the window.

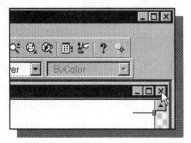

6. Close the window by clicking the **Close** icon located at the upper-right-corner of the *Drawing1* window.

Change the Background Color of the Graphics window

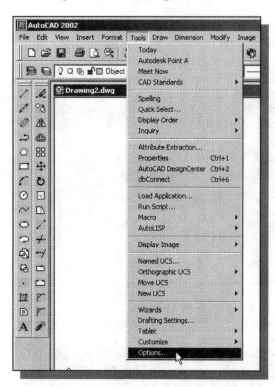

1. In the pull-down menus, select:
    [Tools] → [Options]

❖   Note that many of the AutoCAD interface
    and drawing environment settings can be
    changed through the *Options* dialog box.

2. In the *Options* dialog box, select the
    Display tab if it is not the page on top.

3. In the *Window Elements* section, click the
    Colors button as shown in the figure.

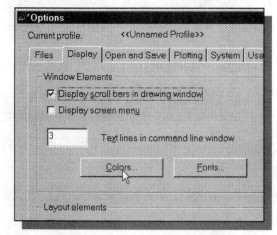

4. In the *Color Options* dialog box, select
    Model tab background as shown.

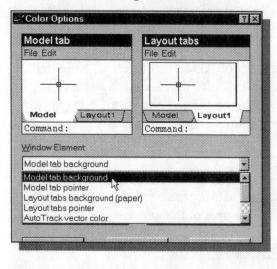

5. In the *Color* option, select ***White*** as
    shown.

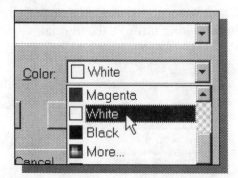

6. Click the **Apply & Close** button to accept the settings.

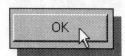

7. Click the **OK** button to exit the *Options*
    dialog box.

GRID and *SNAP* intervals Setup

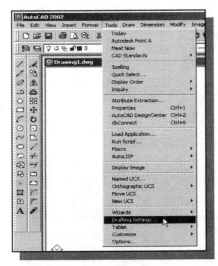

1. In the pull-down menus, select:

    [Tools] → [Drafting Settings]

2. In the *Drafting Settings* dialog box, select the **SNAP and GRID** tab if it is not the page on top.

3. Change *Grid Spacing* to **1.0** for both X and Y directions.

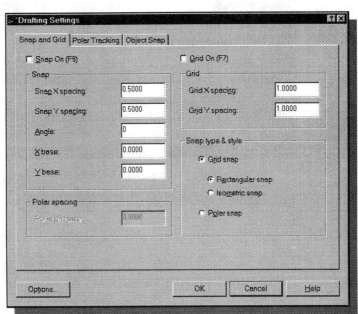

4. Also adjust the *Snap Spacing* to **0.5** for both X and Y directions.

5. Pick **OK** to exit the *Drafting Settings* dialog box.

Layers setup

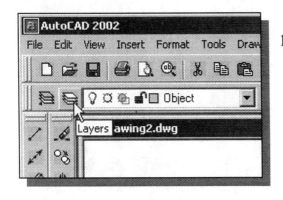

1. Pick *Layers* in the *Object Properties* toolbar.

2. In the *Layer Properties Manager* dialog box, click on the **New** button to create new layers.

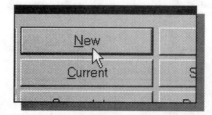

3. Create **layers** with the following settings:

Layer	Color	LineType	Lineweight
Construction	Gray	Continuous	Default
Object_Lines	Blue	Continuous	0.6mm
Hidden_Lines	Cyan	Hidden	0.3mm
Center_Lines	Red	Center	Default
Dimensions	Magenta	Continuous	Default
Section_Lines	Black/White	Continuous	Default
CuttingPlane_Lines	Dark Gray	Phantom	0.6mm
Title_Block	Green	Continuous	1.2mm
Viewport	Black/White	Continuous	Default

4. Highlight the layer *Construction* in the list of layers.

5. Click on the **Current** button to set layer *Construction* as the *Current Layer*.

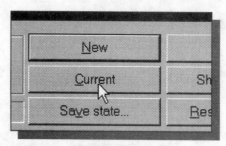

6. Click on the **OK** button to accept the settings and exit the *Layer Properties Manager* dialog box.

7. In the *Status Bar* area, reset the option buttons so that only *SNAP, GRID* and *MODEL* are switched *ON*.

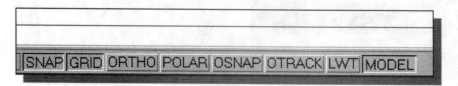

The *Bracket* Design

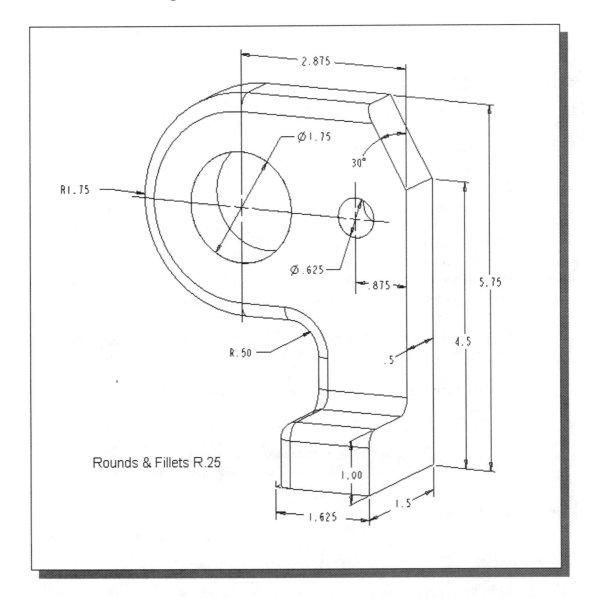

> ➤ Before going through the tutorial, make a rough sketch of a multiview drawing of the part. How many 2D views will be necessary to fully describe the part? Based on your knowledge of **AutoCAD® 2002** so far, how would you arrange and construct these 2D views? Take a few minutes to consider these questions and do preliminary planning by sketching on a piece of paper. You are also encouraged to construct the orthographic views on your own prior to going through the tutorial.

Drawing Construction Lines

We will place the construction lines on the *Construction* layer so that the layer can later be frozen or turned off.

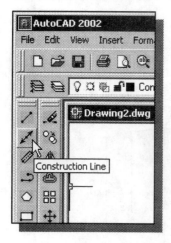

1. Select the **Construction Line** icon in the *Draw* toolbar. In the command prompt area, the message "*_xline Specify a point or [Hor/Ver/Ang/Bisect/Offset]:*" is displayed.

   To orient construction lines, we generally specify two points, although other orientation options are also available.

2. Place the first point at world coordinate (**3,2**) on the screen.

3. Pick a location above the last point to create a **vertical line**.

4. Move the cursor toward the right of the first point and pick a location to create a **horizontal line**.

5. In the *Status Bar* area, turn **OFF** the *SNAP* option.

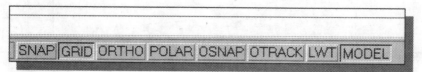

Using the *Offset* command

1. Select the **Offset** icon in the *Modify* toolbar. In the command prompt area, the message "*Specify offset distance or [Through]:*" is displayed.

2. In the command prompt area, enter: **2.875 [ENTER]**.

3. In the command prompt area, the message "*Select object to offset or <exit>:*" is displayed. Pick the **vertical line** on the screen.

4. AutoCAD next asks us to identify the direction of the offset. Pick a location that is to the **right** of the vertical line.

5. Inside the graphics window, **right-mouse-click** to end the *Offset* command.

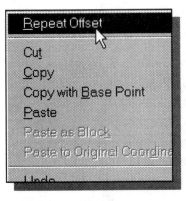

6. Hit the **[SPACE BAR]**, or **right-mouse-click** inside the graphics window and select **Repeat Offset** in the popup list, to repeat the *Offset* command.

7. In the command prompt area, enter: **5.75 [ENTER]**.

8. In the command prompt area, the message *"Select object to offset or <exit>:"* is displayed. Pick the **horizontal line** on the screen.

9. AutoCAD next asks us to identify the direction of the offset. Pick a location that is **above** the horizontal line.

10. Inside the graphics window, **right-mouse-click** to end the *Offset* command.

11. Repeat the *Offset* command and create the lines as shown.

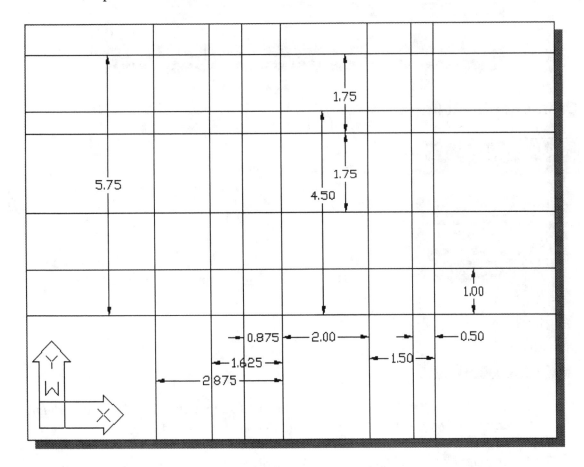

Set layer *Object_Lines* as the *Current Layer*

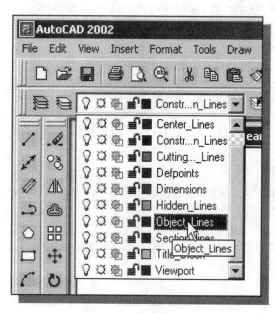

1. On the *Object Properties* toolbar, choose the **Layer Control** box with the left-mouse-button.

2. Move the cursor over the name of layer **Object_Lines** and the tool tip "*Object_Lines*" appears.

3. **Left-mouse-click once** and layer *Object_Lines* is set as the *Current Layer*.

4. In the *Status Bar* area, turn **ON** the *OSNAP, OTRACK*, and *LWT* options.

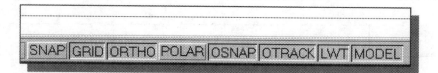

Creating object lines

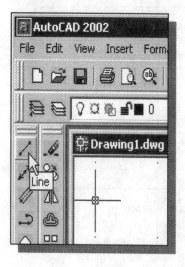

1. Select the **Line** command icon in the *Draw* toolbar. In the command prompt area, the message "*_line Specify first point:*" is displayed.

2. Move the cursor to the intersection of any two lines and notice the visual aid automatically displayed at the intersection.

3. Create the object lines as shown on the next page. (Use the *relative coordinate entry method* and the **Trim** command to construct the 30° line.)

4. Use the **Arc** and **Circle** commands to complete the object lines as shown.

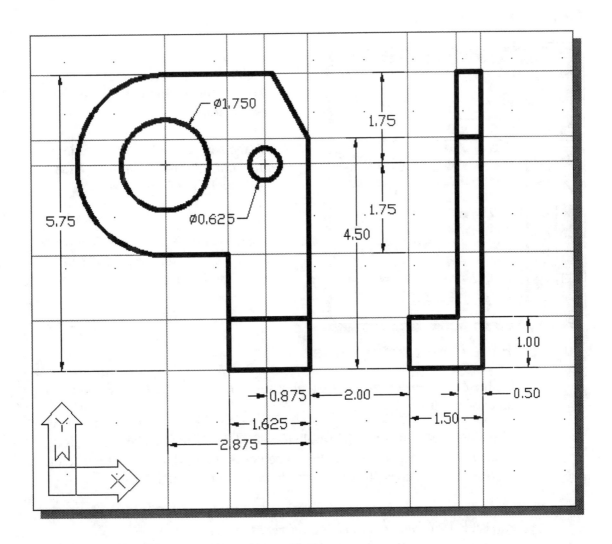

Creating hidden lines

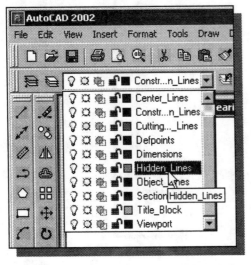

1. On the *Object Properties* toolbar, choose the *Layer Control* box with the left-mouse-button.

2. Move the cursor over the name of layer ***Hidden_Lines***, **left-mouse-click once**, and set layer *Hidden_lines* as the *Current Layer*.

3. Create the five hidden lines in the side view as shown on the next page.

Creating Center lines

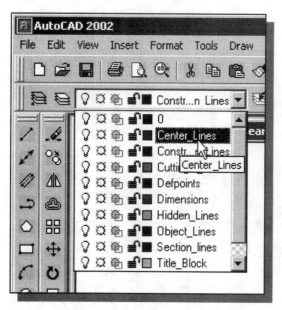

1. On the *Object Properties* toolbar, choose the *Layer Control* box with the left-mouse-button.

2. Move the cursor over the name of layer ***Center_Lines***, **left-mouse-click once**, and set layer *Center_Lines* as the *Current Layer*.

3. Create the center line in the side view as shown. (We will add the center lines in the front-view using the *Center Mark* option.)

Turn *OFF* the Construction Lines

1. On the *Object Properties* toolbar, choose the *Layer Control* box with the left-mouse-button.

2. Move the cursor over the light-bulb icon for layer *Construction_Lines*, **left-mouse-click once**, and notice the icon color is changed to a gray tone color, representing the layer (layer *Construction_Lines*) is turned *OFF*.

3. Move the cursor over the name of layer ***Object_Lines***, **left-mouse-click once**, and set layer *Object_Lines* as the *Current Layer*.

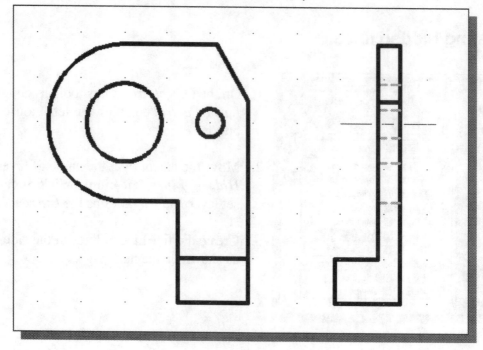

Using the *Fillet* command

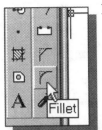

1. Select the **Fillet** command icon in the *Modify* toolbar. In the command prompt area, the message "*Select first object or [Polyline/Radius/Trim]:*" is displayed.

2. Inside the graphics window, **right-mouse-click** to activate the option menu and select the **Radius** option with the left-mouse-button to specify the radius of the fillet.

3. In the command prompt area, the message "*Specify fillet radius:*" is displayed.

   Specify fillet radius: **0.5** [**ENTER**].

4. Pick the **bottom horizontal line** as the first object to fillet.

5. Pick the **adjacent vertical line** connected to the arc to create a rounded corner as shown.

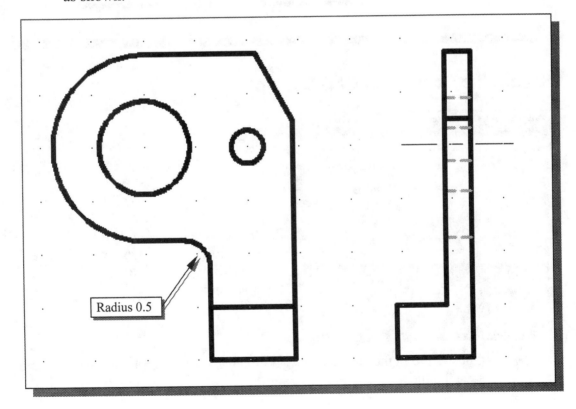

Radius 0.5

6. Repeat the **Fillet** command and create the four rounded corners (Radius 0.25) as shown.

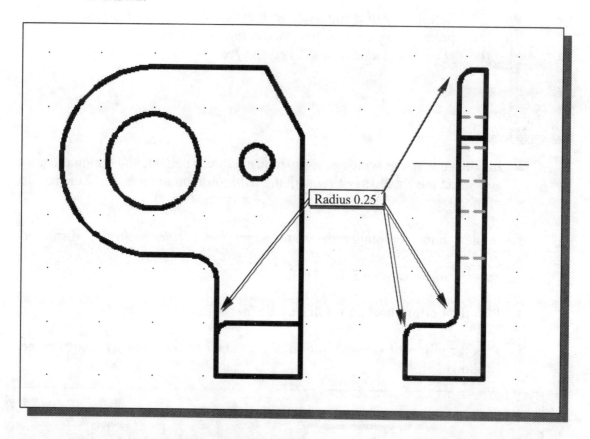

Saving the Completed CAD Design

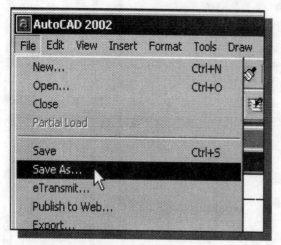

1. In the pull-down menus, select:

    [File] → [Save As]

2. In the *Save Drawing As* dialog box, select the folder in which you want to store the CAD file and enter **Bracket** in the *File name* box.

3. Click **Save** in the *Save Drawing As* dialog box to accept the selections and save the file.

The *Dimension* toolbar

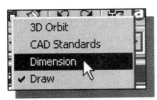

1. Move the cursor to the *Standard* toolbar area and **right-mouse-click** on any icon in the *Standard* toolbar to display a list of toolbar menu groups.

2. Select **Dimension**, with the left-mouse-button, to display the *Dimension* toolbar on the screen.

3. Move the cursor over the icons in the *Dimension* toolbar and read the description of each icon in the *Status Bar* area.

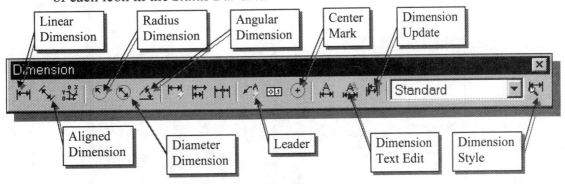

Using *Dimension Style Manager*

The appearance of the dimensions are controlled by *dimension variables*, which we can set using the *Dimension Style Manager* dialog box.

1. In the *Dimension* toolbar, pick **Dimension Style**. The *Dimension Style Manager* dialog box appears on the screen.

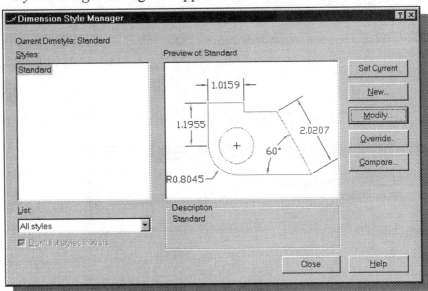

Dimensions nomenclature and basics

As it was stated in *Lesson 1*, the rule for creating CAD designs and drawings is that they should be created **full size** using real-world units. The importance of this practice is evident when we begin applying dimensions to the geometry. The features that we specify for dimensioning are measured and displayed automatically.

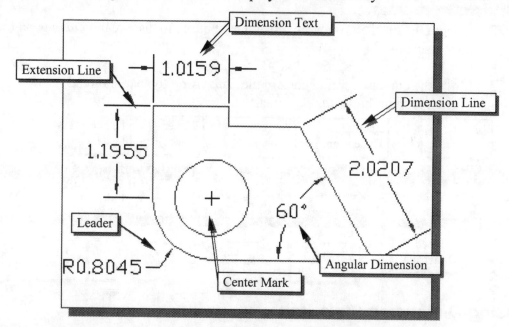

When selecting and placing dimensions, think about (1) the function of the part and (2) the manufacturing operations. Detail drawings should contain only those dimensions that are necessary to make the design. Dimensions for the same feature of the design should be given only once in the same drawing. Nothing should be left to chance or guesswork on a drawing. Drawings should be dimensioned to avoid any possibility of questions. Dimensions should be carefully positioned; preferably near the profile of the feature being dimensioned.

Notice in the *Dimension Style Manager* dialog box, the AutoCAD default style name is *Standard*. We can create our own dimension style to fit the specific type of design we are working on, such as mechanical or architectual.

   2.   Click on the **New** button to create a new dimension style.

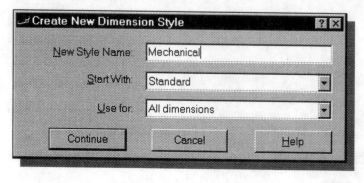

   3.   In the *Create New Dimension Style* dialog box, enter *Mechanical* as the dimension style name.

   4.   Click on the **Continue** button to proceed.

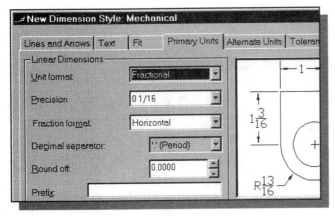

5. Click on the **Primary Units** tab.

6. Select *Fractional* as the *Unit format* under the **Primary Units** tab.

❖ On your own, examine the different options available; most of the settings are self-explanatory.

7. Select the **Fit** tab and notice the two options under *Scale for Dimension Features*.

❖ We can manually adjust the dimension scale factor or let AutoCAD automatically adjust the scale factor. For example, our current drawing will fit on A-size paper, and therefore we will use the scale factor of 1. If we decide to plot the same drawing on B-size paper, then we will need to set the dimension scale factor to 2.0. It is possible to let AutoCAD determine the scale factor based on the *layout* settings; we will discuss more about the *layout* in the next lesson.

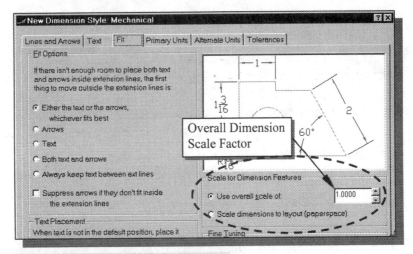

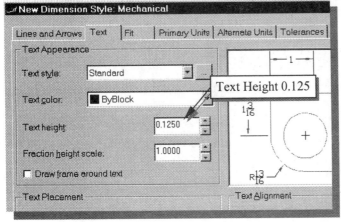

8. Select the **Text** tab.

9. Set the *Text Height* to **0.125**.

10. Select the **Lines and Arrows** tab and set *Arrow size* and *Extend beyond dim lines* to **0.125**. Also set the *Center Mark Type* to **Line**.

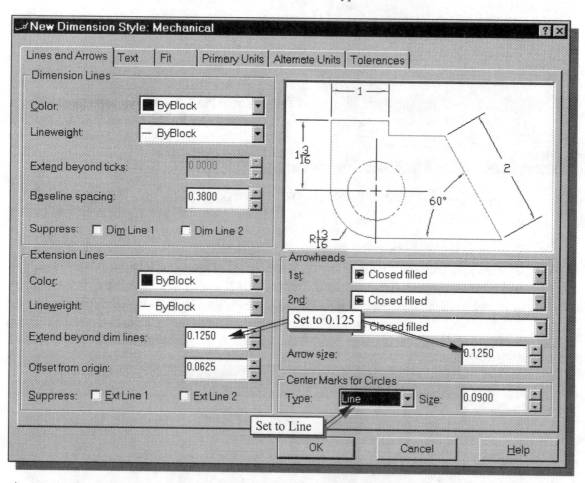

❖ Notice the different options available on this page, options that let us turn off one or both of extension lines, dimension lines, and arrowheads. The *Dimension Style Manager* allows us to easily control the appearance of the dimensions in the drawing.

11. Click on the **OK** button to accept the settings and close the dialog box.

12. Pick the **Set Current** button to make the *Mechanical Dimension Style* the current dimension style.

13. Click on the **OK** button to accept the settings and close the dialog box.

14. Click on the **Close** button to accept the settings and close the *Dimension Style Manager* dialog box.

❖ The *Center Mark* option is used to control the appearance of center marks and centerlines for diameter and radial dimensions.

Using the *Center Mark* command

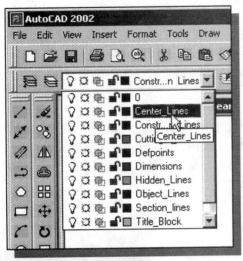

1. On the *Object Properties* toolbar, choose the **Layer Control** box with the left-mouse-button.

2. Move the cursor over the name of layer **Center_Lines**, **left-mouse-click once**, and set layer *Center_lines* as the *Current Layer*.

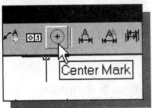

3. In the *Dimension* toolbar, click on the **Center Mark** icon.

4. Pick the radius 1.75 arc in the front-view and notice AutoCAD automatically places two centerlines through the center of the arc.

5. Repeat the **Center Mark** command and pick the small circle to place the centerlines as shown.

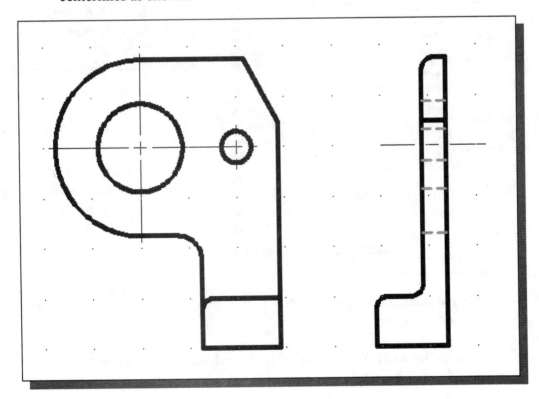

Adding *Linear* dimensions

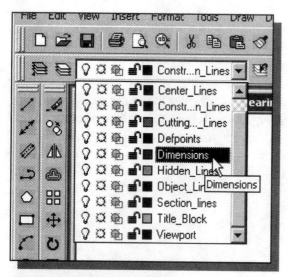

1. On the *Object Properties* toolbar, choose the **Layer Control** box with the left-mouse-button.

2. Move the cursor over the name of layer **Dimensions**, **left-mouse-click once**, and set layer *Dimensions* as the *Current Layer*.

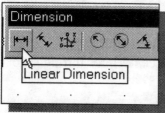

3. In the *Dimension* toolbar, click on the **Linear Dimension** icon.

The *Linear Dimension* command measures and annotates a feature with a horizontal or vertical dimension.

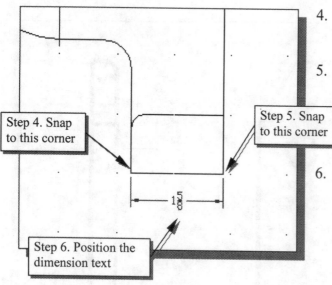

Step 4. Snap to this corner

Step 5. Snap to this corner

Step 6. Position the dimension text

4. Pick the **lower left corner** of the front-view of the part.

5. Pick the **lower right corner** of the front-view of the part.

6. Pick a point that is about 0.5 inch below the bottom horizontal line of the front-view to place the dimension text.

❖ Adding dimensions is this easy with AutoCAD's auto-dimensioning and associative-dimensioning features.

7. Repeat the **Linear Dimension** command and add the necessary linear dimensions as shown.

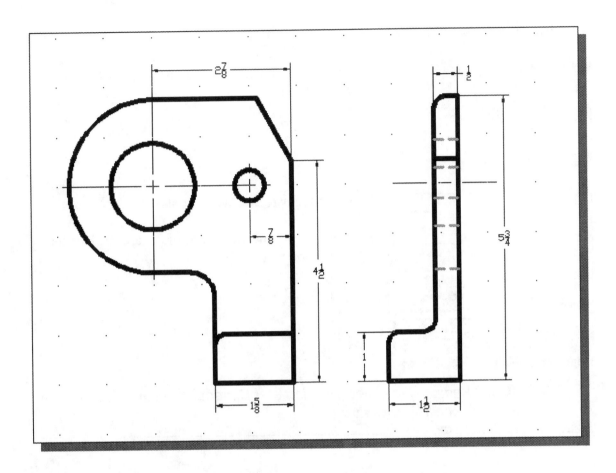

Adding an *Angular* Dimension

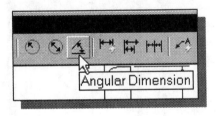

1. In the *Dimension* toolbar, click on the **Angular Dimension** icon.

- The *Angular Dimension* command measures and annotates a feature with an angle dimension.

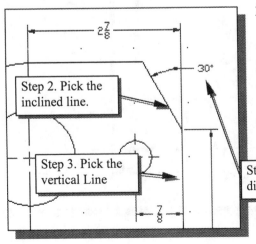

Step 2. Pick the inclined line.

Step 3. Pick the vertical Line

Step 4. Position the dimension text.

2. Pick the **inclined line** of the part in the front-view.

3. Pick the **right vertical line** of the part in the front-view.

4. Pick a point toward the right of the front-view to place the dimension text.

Adding *Radius* and *Diameter* dimensions

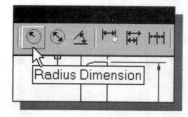

1. In the *Dimension* toolbar, click on the **Radius Dimension** icon.

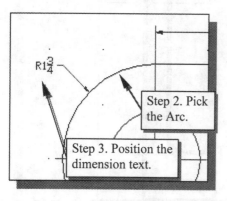

2. Pick the **large arc** in the front-view.

3. Pick a point toward the left of the arc to place the dimension text.

4. Use the *Radius Dimension* and *Diameter Dimension* commands to add the necessary dimensions as shown.

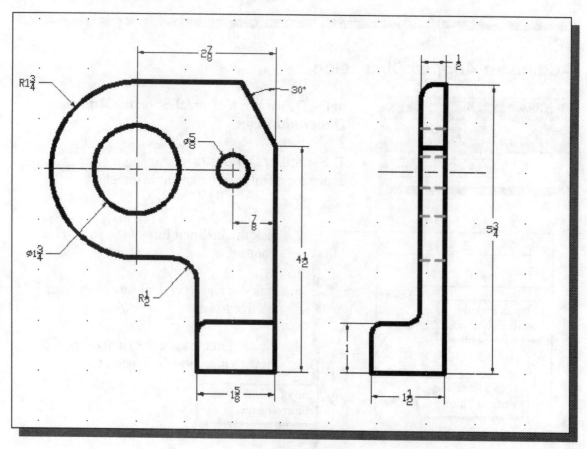

Using the *Single Line Text* command

AutoCAD provides two options to create notes. For simple entries, we can use the **Single Line Text** command. For longer entries with internal formatting, we can use the **Multiline Text** command. The **Single Line Text** command, also known as the **Text** command, can be used to enter several lines of text that can be rotated and resized. The text we are typing is displayed on the screen. Each line of text is treated as a separate object in AutoCAD. To end a line and begin another, press the [**ENTER**] key after entering characters. To end the *Text* command, press the [**ENTER**] key without entering any characters.

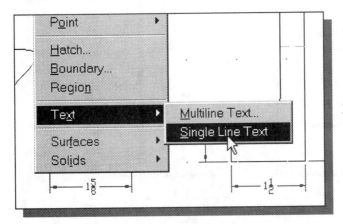

1. In the pull-down menus, select:
    **[Draw] → [Text] →
    [Single Line Text]**

2. In the command prompt area, the message "*Specify start point of text or [Justify/Style]:*" is displayed. Pick a location near the world coordinate (**1,1.5**).

3. In the command prompt area, the message "*Specify Height:*" is displayed. Enter **0.125** as the text height.

4. In the command prompt area, the message "*Specify rotation angle of text <0>:*" is displayed. Enter **0** at the command prompt.

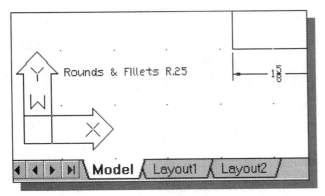

5. In the command prompt area, the message "*Enter Text:*" is displayed.

    Enter: **Rounds &
    Fillets R.25 [ENTER]**.

6. In the *command prompt area*, the message "*Enter Text:*" is displayed. Press the [**ENTER**] key once to end the command.

7. In the *Status Bar* area, reset the options as shown.

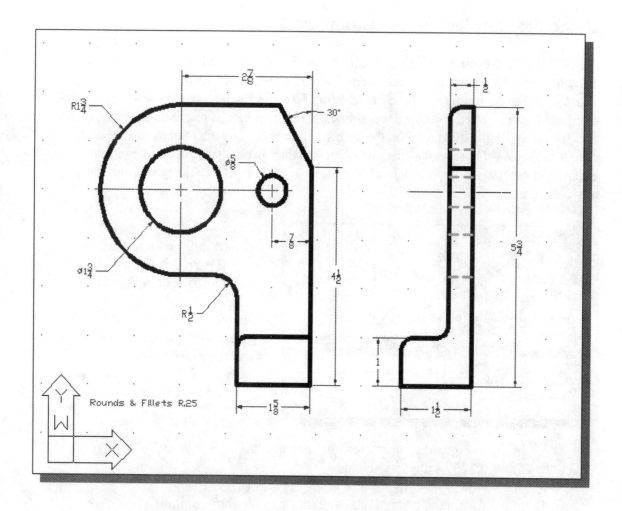

Adding special characters

• We can add special text characters to the dimensioning text and notes. We can type in special characters during any text command and when entering the dimension text. The most common special characters have been given letters to make them easy to remember.

Code	Character	Symbol
%%C	Diameter symbol	Ø
%%D	Degree symbol	°
%%P	Plus/Minus sign	±

➢ On your own, create notes containing some of the special characters listed.

➢ On your own, switch on and off different layers to examine the information stored on each layer.

Saving the Design

➢ In the *Standard Toolbar* area, select the **Save** icon.

A Special Note on Layers containing Dimensions

AutoCAD creates several hidden **BLOCKS** when we create associative dimensions and we will take a more in depth look at *blocks* in *Lesson 9*. AutoCAD treats **blocks** as a special type of object called a *named object*. Each kind of *named object* has a *symbol table* or a *dictionary*, and each table or dictionary can store multiple *named objects*. For example, if we create five dimension styles, our drawing's dimension style *symbol table* will have five dimension style records. In general, we do not work with *symbol tables* or *dictionaries* directly.

When we create dimensions in AutoCAD, most of the hidden blocks are placed in the same layer where the dimension was first defined. Some of the definitions are placed in the *DEFPOINTS* layer. When moving dimensions from one layer to another, AutoCAD does not move these definitions. When deleting layers, we cannot delete the current layer, *layer 0*, xref-dependent layers, or a layer that contains visible and/or invisible objects. Layers referenced by block definitions, along with the *DEFPOINTS* layer, cannot be deleted even if they do not contain visible objects.

To delete layers with hidden blocks, first use the **Purge** command **[File → Drawing Utilities → Purge → Block]** to remove the invisible blocks. (We will have to remove all visible objects prior to using this command.) The empty layer can now be *deleted* or *purged*.

Questions:

1. Why are dimensions and notes important to a technical drawing?

2. List and describe several general-dimensioning practices.

3. Describe the procedure in setting up a new *Dimension Style*.

4. What is the special way to create a diameter symbol when using *DTEXT*?

5. Identify the following commands:

(a)

(b)

(c)

(d)

Exercises:

1.

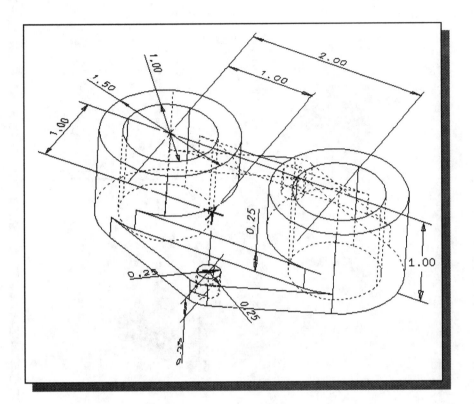

2.

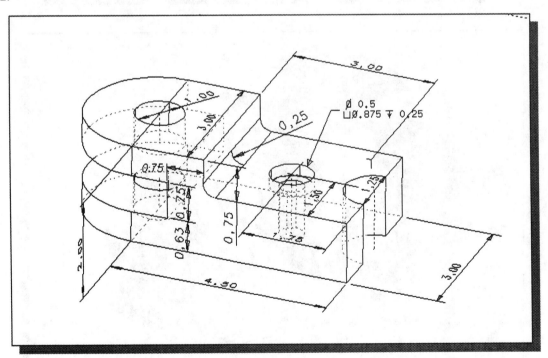

3.

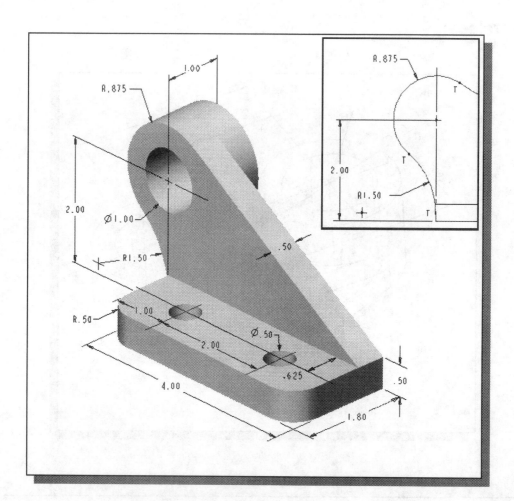

4.

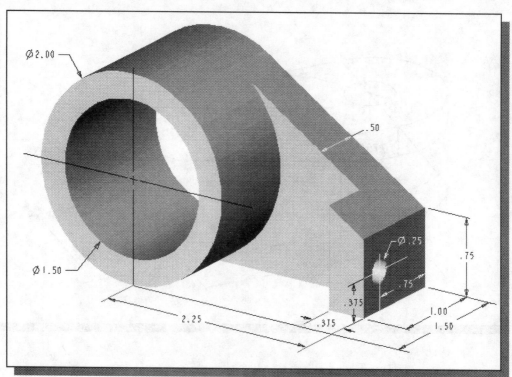

Lesson 7
Templates and Plotting

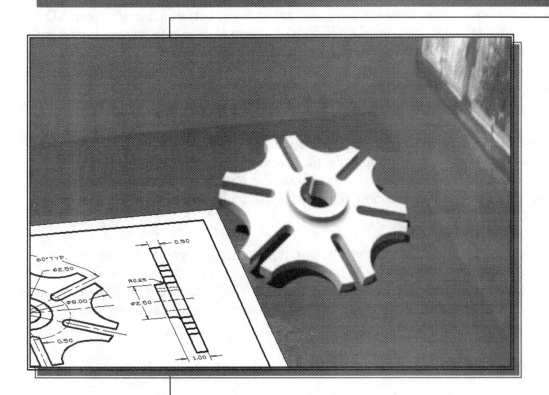

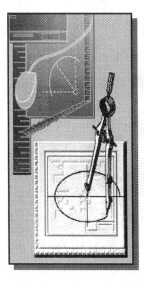

Learning Objectives

- ♦ **Set up the AutoCAD Plot Style option.**
- ♦ **Create a Template file.**
- ♦ **Use the MIRROR command.**
- ♦ **Create Multiple Copies of objects.**
- ♦ **Set up Layouts in Paper Space.**
- ♦ **Create Viewports in Paper Space.**
- ♦ **Use the PROPERTIES command.**
- ♦ **Adjust the Text Scale for Plotting.**

Introduction

One of the main advantages of using CAD systems is that we can easily reuse information that is already in the system. For example, many of the system settings, such as setting up layers, colors, linetypes and grids, are typically performed in all AutoCAD files. In **AutoCAD® 2002**, we can set up **template files** to eliminate these repetitive steps and make our work much more efficient. Using template files also helps us maintain consistent design and drafting standards. In this lesson, we will illustrate the procedure to set up template files that can contain specific plotting settings, system units, environment settings and other drafting standard settings.

We can also reuse any of the geometry information that is already in the system. For example, we can easily create multiple identical copies of geometry with the *Array* command, or create mirror images of objects using the *Mirror* command. In this lesson, we will examine the use of these more advanced construction features and techniques in **AutoCAD® 2002**.

Also in this lesson, we will demonstrate the printing/plotting procedure to create a hardcopy of our design. **AutoCAD® 2002** provides plotting features that are very easy to use. The **AutoCAD® 2002** plotting features include: WYSIWYG (What You See Is What You Get) layouts; onscreen lineweights; plot style tables; device-accurate paper sizes; and creating custom paper sizes.

The *GENEVA CAM* Design

Starting Up AutoCAD 2002

1. Select the **AutoCAD 2002** option on the *Program* menu or select the **AutoCAD 2002** icon on the *Desktop*.

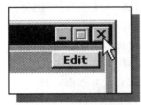

2. In the *AutoCAD Today* startup dialog box, close the dialog box by clicking the **Close** icon with a single click of the left-mouse-button.

❖ Note the units setting of *Drawing1* is set to either the default English units system or the default Metric units. As it was stated in *Lesson 1*, the rule for creating CAD designs and drawings is that they should be created **full size**. The importance of this practice is evident when we are ready to create hardcopies of the design, or transfer the designs electronically to manufacturing equipment, such as a CNC machine. Internally, CAD systems do not distinguish whether the one unit of measurement is one inch or one millimeter. The UNITS setting is used as a conversion factor for the information stored in the CAD database. **AutoCAD**® **2002** provides several options to control the units settings.

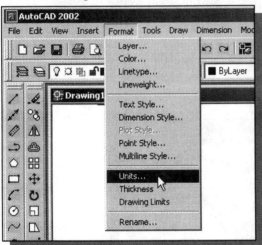

3. In the pull-down menus, select:

[Format] → [Units]

4. In the *Drawing Units* dialog box, set the *Length Type* to **Decimal**.

❖ Note that the measurement of units does not indicate whether it is the English units or the Metric units.

5. Set the precision to **two digits** after the decimal point.

6. Also set the *Drawing units for Design Center blocks* to **Inches** as shown in the figure.

7. Pick **OK** to exit the *Drawing Units* dialog box.

Setting up the *Plot Style Mode*

❖ Using **AutoCAD® 2002** *plot styles* and *plot style tables* allows us to control the way drawings look at plot time. We can reassign object properties, such as color, linetype, and lineweight, and plot the same drawing differently. The default **AutoCAD® 2002** *Plot Style Mode* is set to use the *Color-Dependent plot style*, which controls the plotting of objects based on the object colors and is the traditional method of adjusting the plotted hardcopy in AutoCAD. The new method introduced in **AutoCAD® 2002** is to use the *Named plot style table* that works independently of color. In this lesson, we will learn to plot with the new AutoCAD *Named plot style*, which provides a very flexible and fast way to control the plotting of our designs.

➢ Notice the *Plot Style* box, in the *Object Properties* toolbar, displays the default setting of *ByColor* and is grayed out. This indicates the plot style is set to the *Color-Dependent* plot style, and therefore the object color is used to control plotting.

1. In the pull-down menus, select:

   [Tools] → [Options]

2. In the *Options* dialog box, select the **Plotting** tab if it is not the page on top.

3. In the *Default plot style behavior for new drawings* section, select *Use named plot styles*.

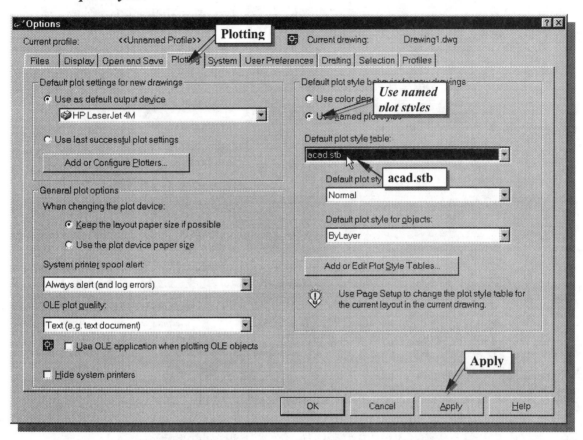

4. In the *Default plot style table*, select ***acad.stb*** from the list of plot style tables.

5. Click on the **Apply** button to reset the modified plotting settings.

6. Pick **OK** to accept the selected settings and close the dialog box.

❖ Notice the *Plot Style* box in the *Object Properties* toolbar still displays the setting of *ByColor* and is still grayed out. This is because the plotting settings are stored in each file. We will close this file and start a new file to have the new settings take effect.

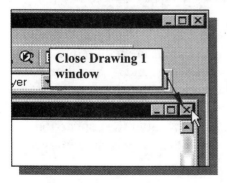

7. Click on the **[X]** button, located near the top-right corner of the *Drawing 1* window, to close the file.

8. In the AutoCAD *Warning* dialog box, select **NO** to close the file without saving.

Starting a new file

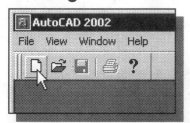

1. Select the **New** icon in the *Standard* toolbar area.

2. In the *AutoCAD Today* startup dialog box, select the **Create Drawings** tab.

3. Select the **Start from Scratch** option as shown.

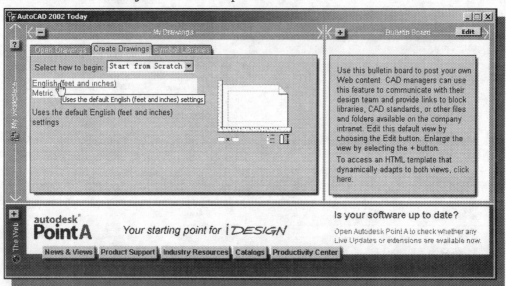

4. Pick **English (Feet and Inches)** as the drawing units

5. On your own, **close** the *AutoCAD 2002 Today* dialog box.

❖ Notice the *Plot Style* box in the *Object Properties* toolbar now displays the setting of **ByLayer** and is no longer grayed out. This indicates we are now using the *Named plot style*, and different options are available to control plotting of the design.

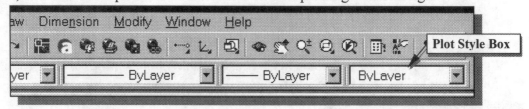

➢ We will demonstrate the use of the **Named plot style** to create a hardcopy of the **Geneva Cam** design. The steps described in the above sections are required to set up the settings for the named plot style to be used in new drawings, and it should be done prior to creating the design. We can also convert an existing drawing to use named plot styles; it will require installing the **AutoCAD Migration** application and use the **Convertpstyles** command to perform the conversion. Note that after the conversion, any color-dependent plot style tables attached to layouts in the drawing are removed.

GRID and SNAP intervals Setup

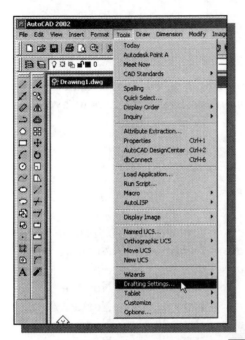

1. In the pull-down menus, select:

    [Tools] → [Drafting Settings]

2. In the *Drafting Settings* dialog box, select the **SNAP and GRID** tab if it is not the page on top.

3. Change *Grid Spacing* to **1.0** for both X and Y directions.

4. Also adjust the *Snap Spacing* to **0.5** for both X and Y directions.

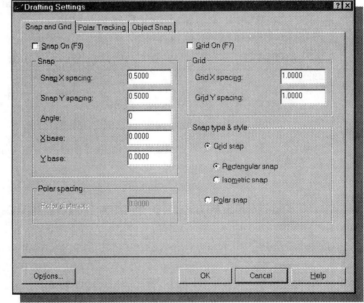

5. Pick **OK** to exit the *Drawing Units* dialog box.

6. In the *Status Bar* area, reset the option buttons so that only *SNAP, GRID*, and *MODEL* are switched *ON*.

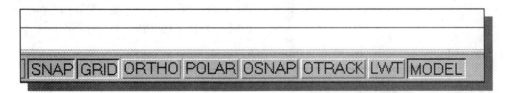

Layers setup

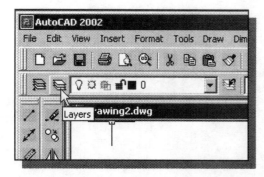

1. Pick *Layers* in the *Object Properties* toolbar.

2. In the *Layer Properties Manager* dialog box, click on *the* **New** icon to create new layers.

3. Create **layers** with the following settings:

Layer	Color	LineType	Lineweight	PlotStyle
Construction	Gray	Continuous	Default	Normal
Object_Lines	Blue	Continuous	0.6mm	Normal
Hidden_Lines	Cyan	Hidden	0.3mm	Normal
Center_Lines	Red	Center	Default	Normal
Dimensions	Magenta	Continuous	Default	Normal
Section_Lines	White/Black	Continuous	Default	Normal
CuttingPlane_Lines	Dark Gray	Phantom	0.6mm	Normal
Title_Block	Green	Continuous	1.2mm	Normal
Viewport	White/Black	Continuous	Default	Normal

➢ Using the *NORMAL PlotStyle* enables plotting of **lineweights** defined in the specific layer.

4. Click on the **OK** button to accept the settings and exit the *Layer Properties Manager* dialog box.

Adding borders and title block in the layout

AutoCAD® 2002 allows us to create plots to any exact scale on the paper. Until now, we have been working in *model space* to create our design in **full size**. When we are ready to plot, we can arrange our design on a two-dimensional sheet of paper so that the plotted hardcopy is exactly what we wanted. This two-dimensional sheet of paper is known as the *paper space* in AutoCAD. We can place borders and title blocks on *paper space*, the objects that are less critical to our design.

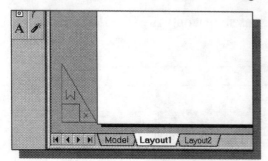

1. Pick the **Layout1** tab to switch to the two-dimensional paper space. The *Page Setup* dialog box appears.

2. In the *Page Setup* dialog box, select a plotter/printer that is available to plot/print your design. Consult with your instructor or technical support personnel if you have difficulty identifying the hardware.

❖ In this lesson, we will demonstrate the plotting procedure for an A-size plot on a LaserJet printer. The procedure described here is also applicable to other types of printers and plotters.

Notice the *Printable area* listed in the *Paper size and paper units* section is typically smaller than the actual paper size, which is due to the limitations of the hardware.

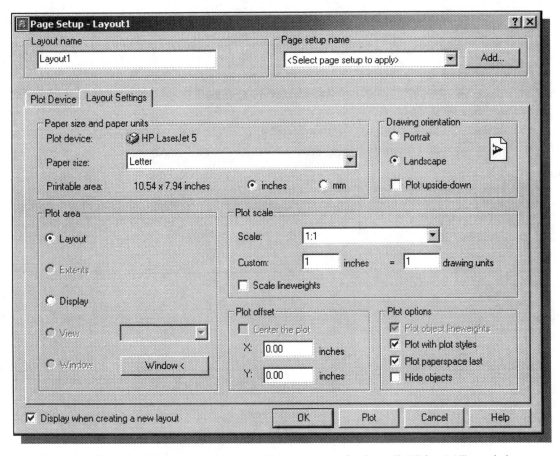

3. Confirm the *Paper size* is set to *Letter* or equivalent (8.5" by 11") and the *Drawing orientation* is set to *Landscape*.

4. Click on the **OK** button to accept the settings and exit the *Page Setup* dialog box.

❖ In the graphics window, a rectangular outline on a gray background indicates the paper size. The dashed lines displayed within the paper indicate the *Printable area*.

5. In the *Object Properties* toolbar area, select the **Layer Control** box and set layer *Title_Block* as the *Current Layer*.

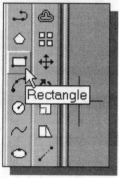

6. Select the **Rectangle** icon in the *Draw* toolbar. In the command prompt area, the message "*Specify first corner point or [Chamfer/Elevation/Fillet/Thickness/Width]:*" is displayed.

7. Pick a location that is on the inside and near the lower left corner of the dashed rectangle.

8. In the command prompt area, use the *relative coordinate entry method* and create a 10.25"X7.75" rectangle.

9. Complete the title block as shown.

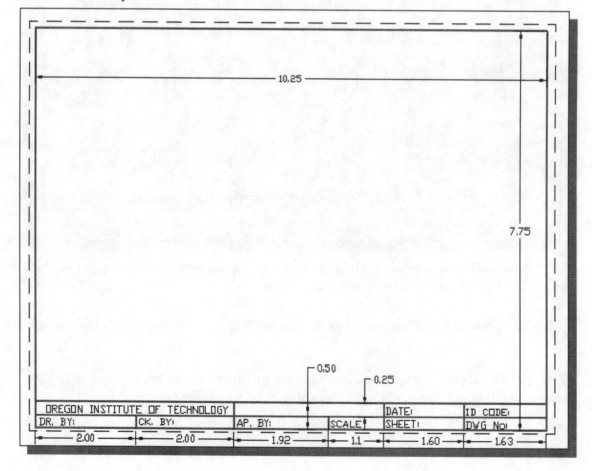

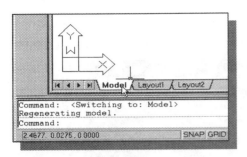

10. Pick the **Model** tab to switch back to *model space*.

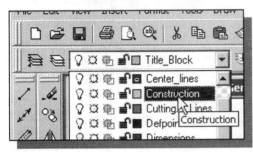

11. In the *Object Properties* toolbar area, select the **Layer Control** box and set layer *Construction_Lines* as the *Current Layer*.

➢ Notice the title block we created is shown only in *paper space*.

Create a Template file

The heart of any CAD system is the ability to reuse information that is already in the system. In the preceding sections, we spent a lot of time setting up system variables, such as layers, colors, linetypes and plotting settings. We will make a **template file** containing all of the settings and the title block we have created so far.

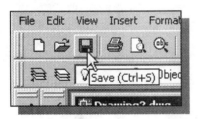

1. In the *Standard* toolbar area, select the **Save** icon.

2. In the *Save Drawing As* dialog box, select the folder in which you want to store the *template file* (.dwt) and enter **Acad_A_Title** in the *File name* box.

3. Pick **Save** in the *Save Drawing As* dialog box to close the dialog box.

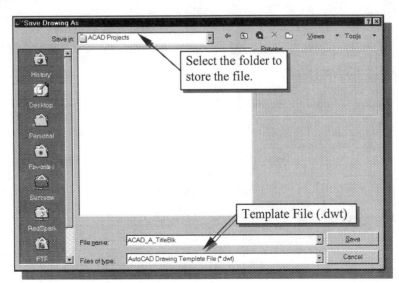

Select the folder to store the file.

Template File (.dwt)

4. In the *Template Description* dialog box, enter ***A-size layout with title block*** in the *Description* box.

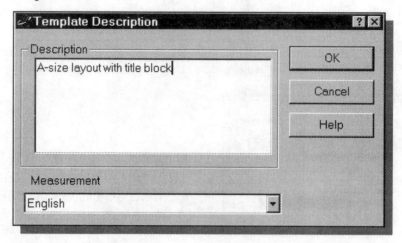

5. Pick **OK** to close the dialog box and save the template file.

➢ The only difference between an AutoCAD template file and a regular AutoCAD drawing file is the filename extension, (.dwt) versus (.dwg). We can convert any AutoCAD drawing into an AutoCAD template file by changing the filename extension to (.dwt.) It is recommended that you keep a second copy of any template files on a separate floppy disk as a backup.

Exit AutoCAD 2002

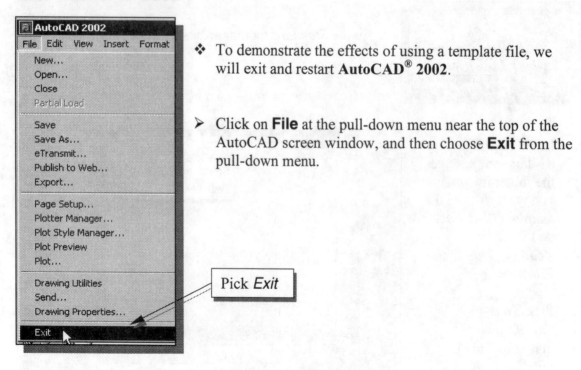

❖ To demonstrate the effects of using a template file, we will exit and restart **AutoCAD® 2002**.

➢ Click on **File** at the pull-down menu near the top of the AutoCAD screen window, and then choose **Exit** from the pull-down menu.

Pick *Exit*

Starting Up AutoCAD 2002

1. Select the **AutoCAD 2002** option on the *Program* menu or select the **AutoCAD 2002** icon on the *Desktop*.

2. In the *AutoCAD Today* startup dialog box, select the **Template** option.

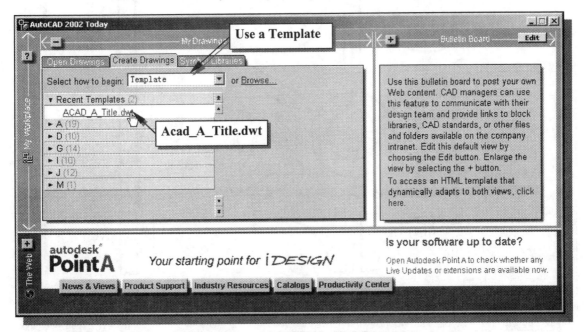

3. Select the *Acad_A_Title* template file from the list of template files. If the template file is not listed, click on the **Browse** button to locate it and proceed to open a new drawing file.

4. Pick **Layers** in the *Object Properties* toolbar.

5. Examine the layer property settings in the *Layer Properties Manager* dialog box.

6. Click on the **OK** button to exit the *Layer Properties Manager* dialog box.

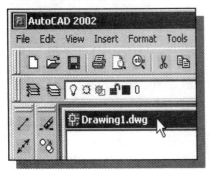

7. Switch to the *Drawing1* window by left-clicking once in the title area of the window.

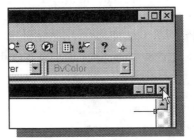

8. Close the window by clicking the **Close** icon located at the upper-right-corner of the *Drawing1* window.

The *Geneva Cam* example

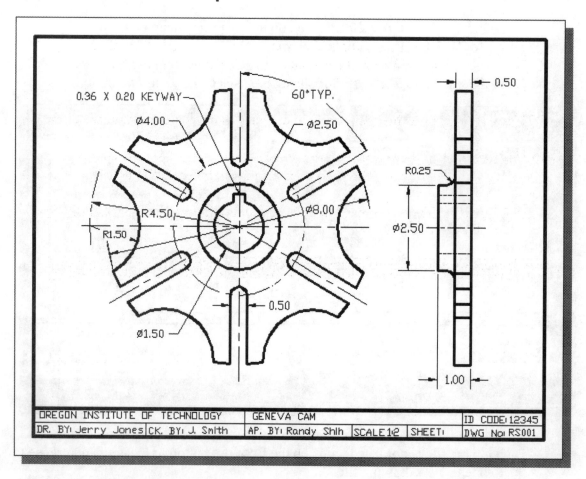

Drawing construction lines

1. Select the **Construction Line** icon in the *Draw* toolbar. In the command prompt area, the message "*_xline Specify a point or [Hor/Ver/Ang/Bisect/Offset]:*" is displayed.

2. Place the first point at world coordinate (**5,4.5**) on the screen.

3. Pick a location above the last point to create a **vertical line**.

4. Move the cursor toward the right of the first point, and then pick a location to create a **horizontal line**.

5. Next create a construction line that is rotated 30 degrees from horizontal, enter **@2<30 [ENTER]**.

6. Inside the graphics window, **right-mouse-click** to end the *Construction Line* command.

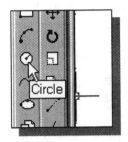

7. Select the **Circle** icon in the *Draw* toolbar. In the command prompt area, the message "*CIRCLE Specify center point for circle or [3P/2P/Ttr]:*" is displayed.

8. Pick the intersection of the lines as the center point of the circle.

9. In the command prompt area, the message "*Specify radius of circle or [Diameter]:*" is displayed. Enter **0.75** [**ENTER**].

10. Repeat the *Circle* command and create four additional circles of radii **1.25**, **2.0**, **4.0** and **4.5** as shown.

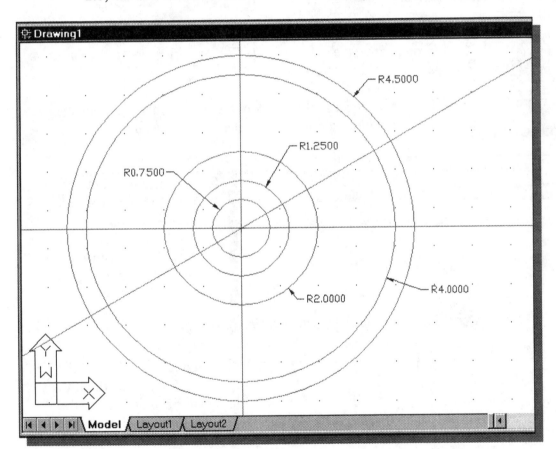

11. In the *Status Bar* area, reset the options and turn **ON** the *GRID, OSNAP, OTRACK*, and *LWT* options.

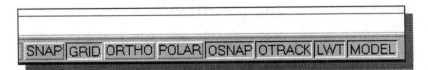

Creating object lines

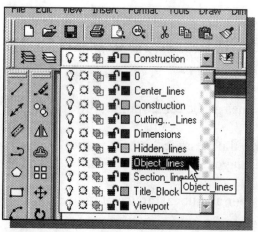

1. On the *Object Properties* toolbar, choose the ***Layer Control*** box with the left-mouse-button.

2. Move the cursor over the name of layer ***Object_Lines***; the tool tip "*Object_Lines*" appears.

3. **Left-mouse-click once** and layer *Object_Lines* is set as the *Current Layer*.

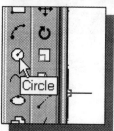

4. Select the ***Circle*** icon in the *Draw* toolbar. In the command prompt area, the message "*CIRCLE Specify center point for circle or [3P/2P/Ttr]:*" is displayed.

5. Move the cursor to the center of the circles, then left-click once to select the intersection as the center of the new circle.

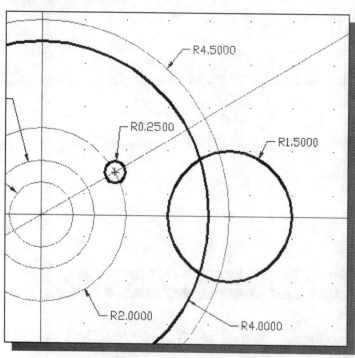

6. In the command prompt area, the message "*Specify radius of circle or [Diameter]:*" is displayed. Pick the **right-intersection** of the horizontal line and the radius 4.0 circle.

7. Repeat the *Circle* command and pick the **right-intersection** of the horizontal line and the radius 4.5 circle as the center point of the circle.

8. In the command prompt area, the message "*Specify radius of circle or [Diameter]:*" is displayed. Enter **1.5** [**ENTER**].

9. Repeat the *Circle* command and create a circle of radius **0.25** centered at the intersection of the inclined line and the radius 2.0 circle as shown.

Using the *Offset* command

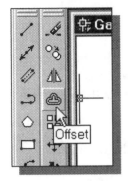

1. Select the **Offset** icon in the *Modify* toolbar. In the command prompt area, the message *"Specify offset distance or [Through]:"* is displayed.

2. In the command prompt area, enter: **0.25 [ENTER]**.

3. In the command prompt area, the message *"Select object to offset or <exit>:"* is displayed. Pick the **inclined line** on the screen.

4. AutoCAD next asks us to identify the direction of the offset. Pick a location that is **below** the inclined line.

5. Inside the graphics window, **right-mouse-click** to end the *Offset* command.

❖ Notice that the new line created by the *Offset* command is placed on the same layer as the line we selected to offset. Which layer is current does not matter; the offset object will always be on the same layer as the original object.

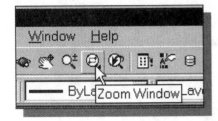

6. Use the **Zoom Window** command and zoom-in on the 30 degrees region as shown.

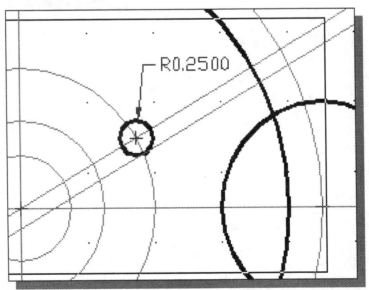

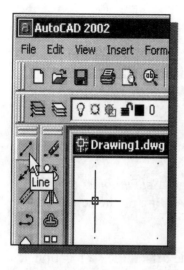

7. Select the **Line** command icon in the *Draw* toolbar. In the command prompt area, the message "*_line Specify first point:*" is displayed.

8. Move the cursor to the intersection of the small circle and the lower inclined line and notice the visual aid that automatically displays at the intersection. Left-click once to select the point.

9. Pick the next intersection point, toward the right side, along the inclined line.

> On your own, use the **Trim** and **Erase** commands to remove the unwanted portions of the objects until your drawing contains only the objects shown below.

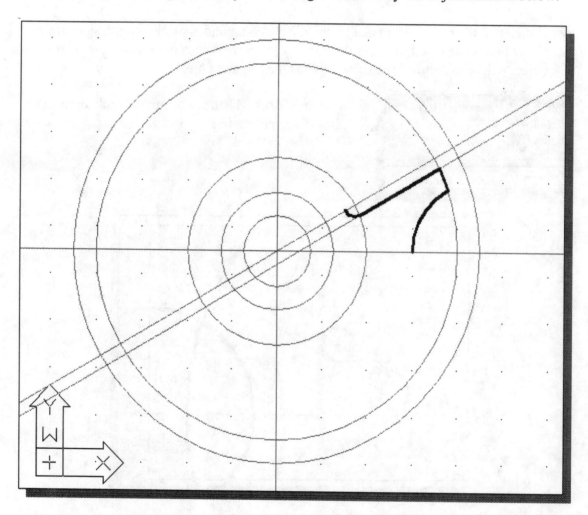

Using the *Mirror* command

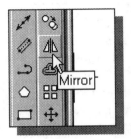

1. Select the **Mirror** command icon in the *Modify* toolbar. In the command prompt area, the message "*Select objects:*" is displayed.

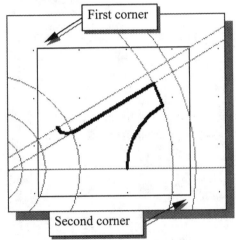

First corner

Second corner

2. Create a *selection* window by selecting the two corners as shown.

Note that in **AutoCAD® 2002**, creating the selection window from left to right will select only objects entirely within the selection area. Going from right to left (crossing selection) selects objects within and objects crossing the selection area. Objects must be at least partially visible to be selected.

3. Inside the graphics window, **right-mouse-click** to accept the selection and continue with the *Mirror* command.

4. In the command prompt area, the message "*Specify the first point of the mirror line:*" is displayed. Pick any intersection point along the horizontal line on the screen.

5. In the command prompt area, the message "*Specify the second point:*" is displayed. Pick any other intersection point along the horizontal line on the screen.

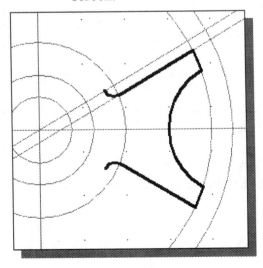

6. In the command prompt area, the message "*Delete source objects? [Yes/No] <N>:*" is displayed. Inside the graphics window, **right-mouse-click** and select [**ENTER**] to retain the original objects.

Enter
Cancel

Yes
No

Pan
Zoom

Using the *Array* command

❖ We can make multiple copies of objects in polar or rectangular arrays (patterns). For polar arrays, we control the number of copies of the object and whether the copies are rotated. For rectangular arrays, we control the number of rows and columns and the distance between them.

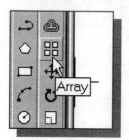

1. Select the **Array** command icon in the *Modify* toolbar. In the command prompt area, the message "*Select objects:*" is displayed.

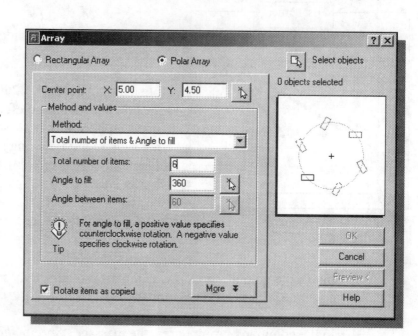

2. In the *Array* dialog box, select the **Polar Array** option.

3. Enter **5.0** and **4.5** as the X and Y coordinates of the *Center point* of the array.

4. Enter **6** as the number of items in the array.

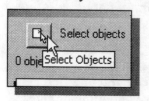

5. Click the **Select Objects** icon, as shown in the figure, to select objects to create the array.

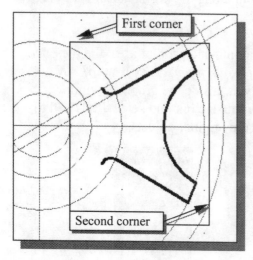

6. Using a *selection* window, enclose the objects we mirrored and the mirrored copies as shown.

7. In the command prompt area, the message "*Select Objects:*" is displayed. Inside the graphics window, **right-mouse-click** to end the selection.

8. In the *Array* dialog box, click the **OK** button to create the array.

9. Next construct the *0.36 X 0.20* keyway by first creating parallel lines at 0.95 and 0.18 distance of the horizontal and vertical construction lines.

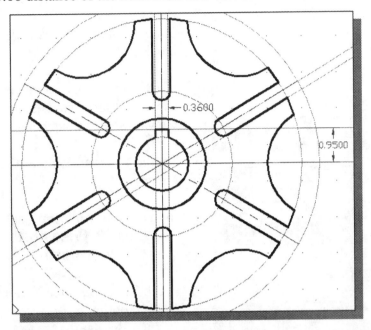

➤ On your own, complete the two views with dimensions. (In the *Dimension Style Manager*, set options under the **Fit** tab to control the appearance of radius and diameter dimensions.)

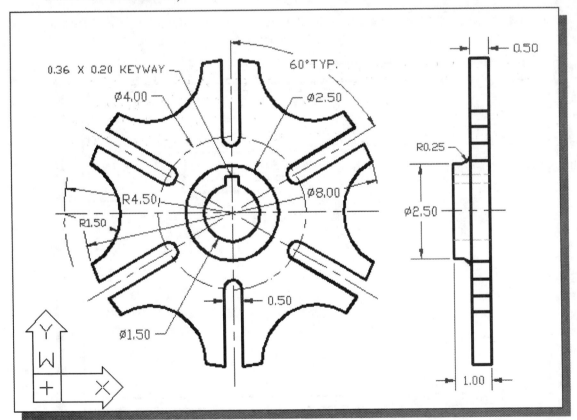

Creating a *Viewport* inside the title block

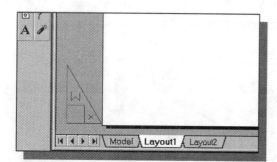

1. Pick the **Layout1** tab to switch to the two-dimensional paper space containing the title block.

2. If a view is displayed inside the title block, use the *Erase* command and delete the view by selecting any edge of the viewport.

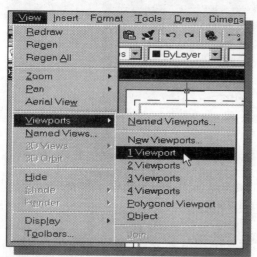

3. Set the *Viewport* layer as the *Current Layer*.

4. In the pull-down menus, select:
   **[View] → [Viewports] →
   [1 Viewport]**

5. In the *Status Bar* area, turn *OFF* the *OSNAP* option.

6. Create a *viewport* inside the title block area as shown.

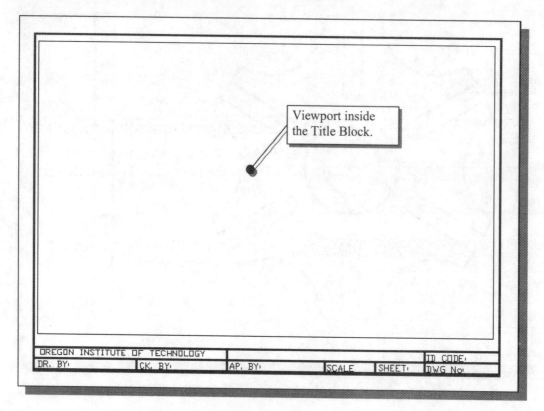

Viewport inside the Title Block.

Viewport properties

1. Pre-select the viewport by left-clicking once on any edge of the viewport.

2. In the *Standard* toolbar, select the **Properties** icon.

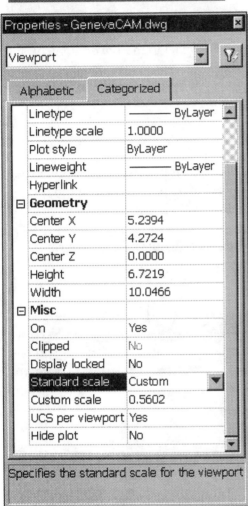

3. In the *Properties* dialog box, scroll down to the bottom of the list. Notice the current scale is set to ***Custom***, ***0.5602***. (The number on your screen might be different.)

4. **Left-click** the *Standard scale* box and notice an arrowhead appears.

5. Click on the arrowhead button and a list of standard scales is displayed. Use the scroll bar to look at the list.

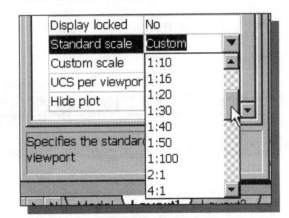

6. Select **1:2** in the standard scale list. This will set the plotting scale factor to half scale.

7. Click on the [**X**] button to exit the *Properties* dialog box.

Hide the *Viewport borders*

We will **turn off** the *viewport borders* so that the lines will not be plotted.

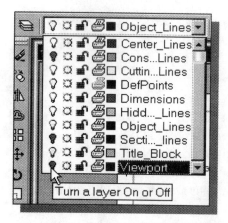

1. With the *viewport* pre-selected, choose the ***Layer Control*** box with the left-mouse-button.

2. Move the cursor over the name of layer ***Viewport***, **left-mouse-click once**, and move the viewport to layer *Viewport*.

3. Turn ***OFF*** layer *Viewport* in the *Layer Control* box.

Adjusting the dimension scale

1. Move the cursor to the *Standard* toolbar area and **right-click** the empty area (in between two icons) of the *Standard* toolbar to display a list of toolbar menu groups.

2. Select **Dimension**, with the left-mouse-button, to display the *Dimension* toolbar on the screen.

3. Click on the ***Dimension Style*** icon.

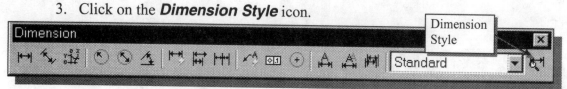

4. In the *Dimension Style Manager* dialog box, select **Modify**.

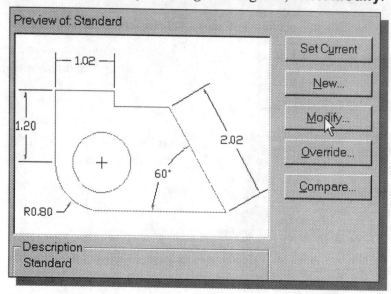

5. Use the ***Scale dimensions to layout (paperspace)*** option in the *Scale for Dimension Features* section under the **Fit** tab.

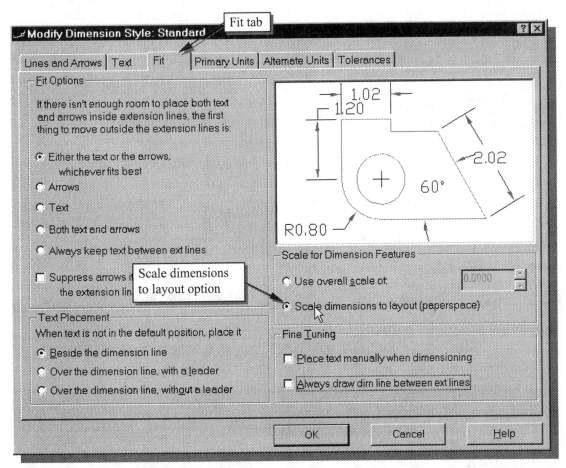

6. Click on the **OK** button to close the *Modify Dimension Style* dialog box.

7. Click on the **Close** button to close the *Dimension Style Manager* dialog box.

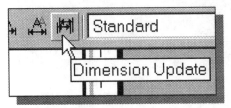

8. Click on the ***Dimension Update*** icon.

9. Pick one of the radius dimensions.

10. Inside the graphics window, right-mouse-click to update the selected dimension.

11. Repeat the ***Dimension Update*** command on all the dimensions.

Plot/Print the drawing

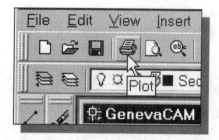

1. In the *Standard* toolbar, select the **Plot** icon.

2. Confirm the proper **plot device** is selected.

3. In the *Plot Area* section, confirm it is set to **Layout**.

4. In the *Plot Scale* section, confirm it is set to *1:1*. Our *paper space* is set to the correct paper size.

5. In the *Plot options* section, confirm the **Plot with plot styles** and **Plot paper space last** options are selected.

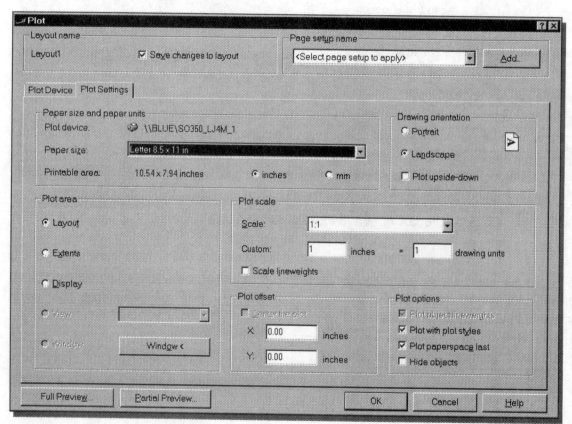

6. Click on the **OK** button to proceed with plotting the drawing.

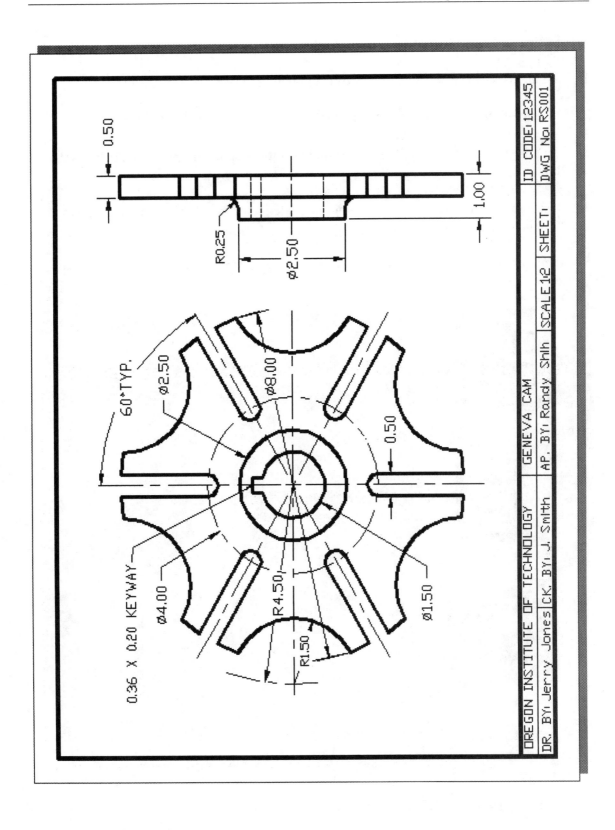

0.50

1.00

R0.25

Ø2.50

ID CODE: 12345

DWG No: RS001

SHEET:

SCALE 1:2

AP. BY: Randy Shih

GENEVA CAM

OREGON INSTITUTE OF TECHNOLOGY

DR. BY: Jerry Jones | CK. BY: J. Smith

60°TYP.

Ø2.50

Ø8.00

0.50

0.36 X 0.20 KEYWAY

Ø4.00

R4.50

R1.50

Ø1.50

Questions:

1. List and describe three advantages of using *template files*.

2. Describe the items that were included in the *Acad_A_Title* template file.

3. List and describe two methods of creating multiple copies of objects in **AutoCAD® 2002**.

4. Describe the procedure in determining the scale factor for plotting an **AutoCAD® 2002** layout.

5. Identify the following commands:

(a)

(b)

(c)

(d)

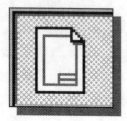

Exercises:

1. Plate thickness : 0.125 inch

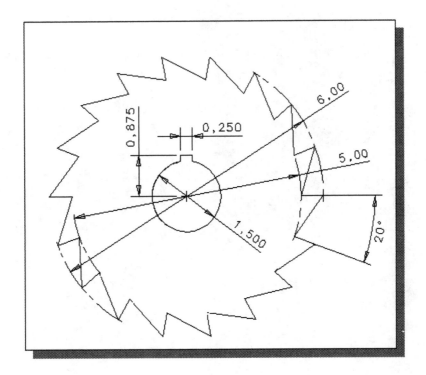

2.

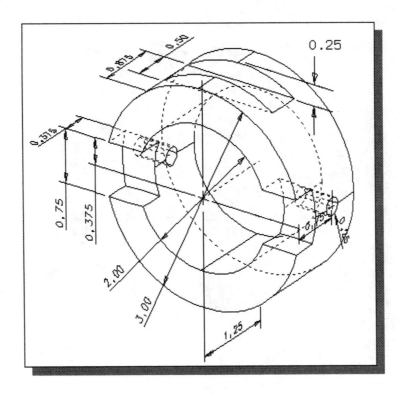

3.

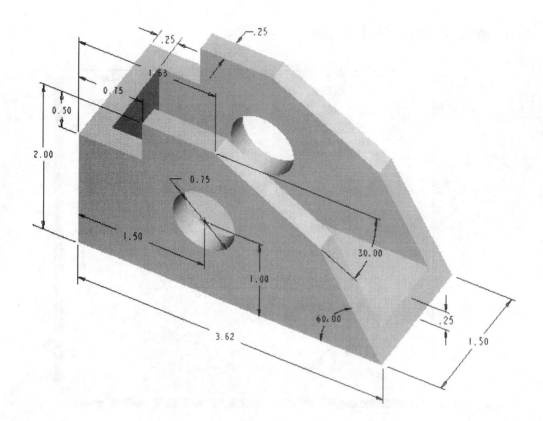

4.

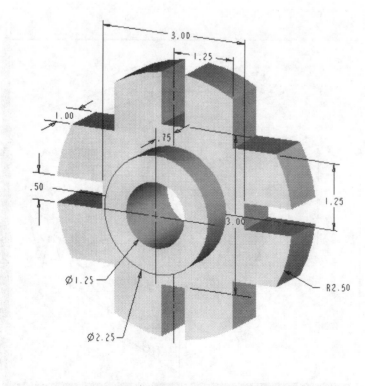

5. Dimensions are in Millimeters. (Thickness: 25 mm.)

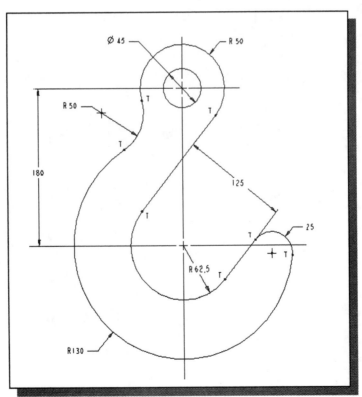

Notes:

Lesson 8
Auxiliary Views and Editing with GRIPS

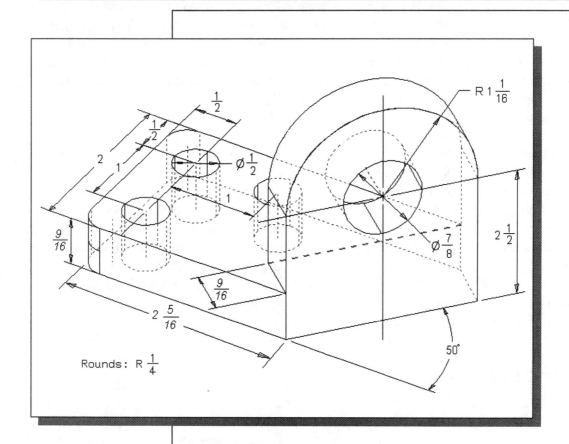

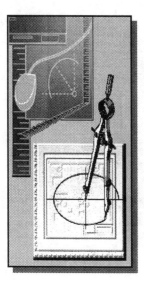

Learning Objectives

- ◆ **Use 2D Projection method to Draw Auxiliary Views.**
- ◆ **Create Rectangles.**
- ◆ **Use the basic GRIPS Editing commands.**
- ◆ **Create and Edit the Plot Style table.**
- ◆ **Setup and use the Polar Tracking option.**
- ◆ **Create multiple Viewports in Paper Space.**

Introduction

An important rule concerning multiview drawings is to draw enough views to accurately describe the design. This usually requires two or three of the regular views, such as a front-view, a top-view and/or a side-view. Many designs have features located on inclined surfaces that are not parallel to the regular planes of projection. To truly describe the feature, the true shape of the feature must be shown using an **auxiliary view**. An *auxiliary view* has a line of sight that is perpendicular to the inclined surface, as viewed looking directly at the inclined surface. An *auxiliary view* is a supplementary view that can be constructed from any of the regular views. This lesson will demonstrate the construction of an auxiliary view using various CAD techniques.

In this lesson, we will examine the use of the very powerful AutoCAD *GRIPS* feature. In **AutoCAD® 2002**, a *GRIP* is a small square displayed on a pre-selected object. Grips are key control locations such as the endpoints and midpoints of lines and arcs. Different types of objects display different numbers of grips. Using grips, we can *stretch*, *move*, *mirror*, *scale*, *rotate*, and *copy* objects without entering commands or clicking toolbars. Grips reduce the keystrokes and object selection required in performing common editing commands. To edit with grips, we select the objects <u>before</u> issuing any commands. To remove a specific object from a selection set that displays grips, we hold down the **[SHIFT]** key as we select the object. To exit the grip modes and return to the *command prompt*, press the **[ESC]** key.

The *V-BLOCK* Design

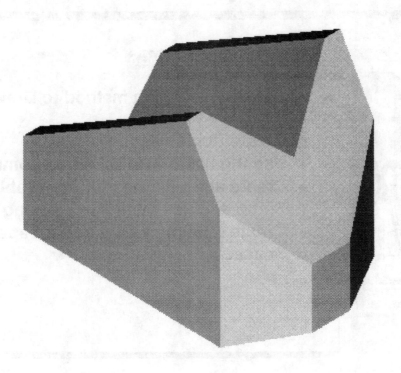

Starting Up AutoCAD 2002

1. Select the **AutoCAD 2002** option on the *Program* menu or select the **AutoCAD 2002** icon on the *Desktop*.

2. In the *AutoCAD 2002 Today* startup dialog box, select the **Template** option.

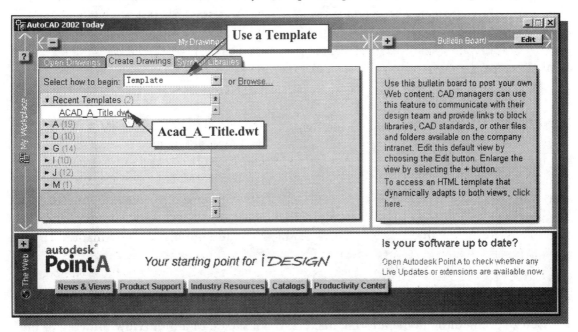

3. Select the *Acad_A_Title* template file from the list of template files. If the template file is not listed, click on the **Browse** button to locate and proceed to open a new drawing file.

4. Pick **Layers** in the *Object Properties* toolbar.

5. Examine the layer property settings in the *Layer Properties Manager* dialog box.

6. Click on the **OK** button to exit the *Layer Properties Manager* dialog box.

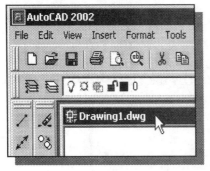

7. Switch to the *Drawing1* window by left-clicking once in the title area of the window.

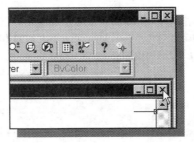

8. Close the window by clicking the **Close** icon located at the upper-right-corner of the *Drawing1* window.

The *V-Block* example

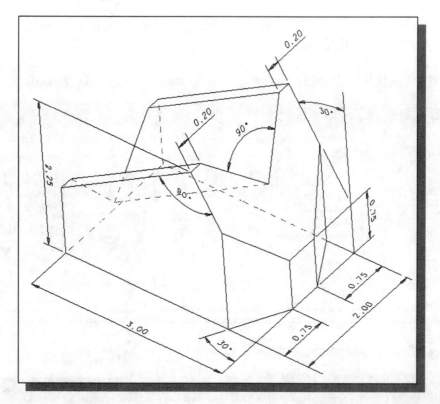

> ➤ Before going through the tutorial, make a rough sketch of a multiview drawing of the part. How many 2D views will be necessary to fully describe the part? Based on your knowledge of **AutoCAD® 2002** so far, how would you arrange and construct these 2D views? Take a few minutes to consider these questions and do preliminary planning by sketching on a piece of paper. You are also encouraged to construct the orthographic views on your own prior to going through the tutorial.

Setting up the principal views

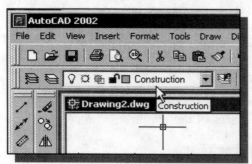

1. In the *Layer Control* box, confirm layer *Construction_Lines* is set as the *Current Layer*.

2. In the *Status Bar* area, reset the options and turn **ON** the *OSNAP, OTRACK, LWT*, and *MODEL* options.

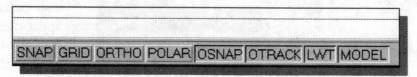

- We will first create construction geometry for the front-view.

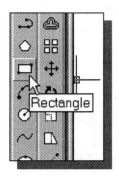

3. Select the **Rectangle** icon in the *Draw* toolbar. In the command prompt area, the message "*Specify first corner point or [Chamfer/Elevation/Fillet/Thickness/Width]:*" is displayed.

4. Place the first corner-point of the rectangle near the lower left corner of the screen. Do not be overly concerned about the actual coordinates of the location; the drawing space is as big as you can imagine.

5. We will create a 3" x 2.25" rectangle. Enter **@3,2.25 [ENTER]**.

❖ The *Rectangle* command creates rectangles as *polyline* features, which means all segments of a rectangle are created as a single object.

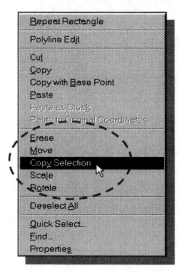

6. We will next use the *GRIPS* editing tools to make a copy of the rectangle. Pick any edge of the rectangle we just created. Notice that small squares appear at different locations on the rectangle.

7. Inside the graphics window, **right-mouse-click** to bring up the popup option menu.

❖ In the center section of the popup menu, the set of GRIPS editing commands includes Erase, Move, Copy Selection, Scale, and Rotate.

8. In the popup menu, select the **Copy Selection** option.

9. In the command prompt area, the message "*Specify base point or displacement, or [Multiple]:*" is displayed. Pick the **lower right corner** as the base point. A copy of the rectangle is attached to the cursor at the base point.

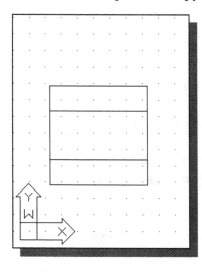

10. In the command prompt area, the message "*Specify second point of displacement, or <use first point as displacement>:*" is displayed. Enter: **@0,0.75 [ENTER]**.

❖ This will position the second rectangle at the location for the 30-degree angle.

11. Preselect the copy by picking the top horizontal line on the screen. The second rectangle, the copy we just created, is selected.

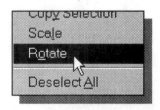

12. Inside the graphics window, **right-mouse-click** to bring up the popup option menu and select the **Rotate** option.

13. In the command prompt area, the message *"Specify base point:"* is displayed. Pick the **lower right corner** of the selected rectangle as the base point.

14. In the command prompt area, the message *"Specify the rotation angle or [Reference]:"* is displayed. Enter: **30 [ENTER]**.

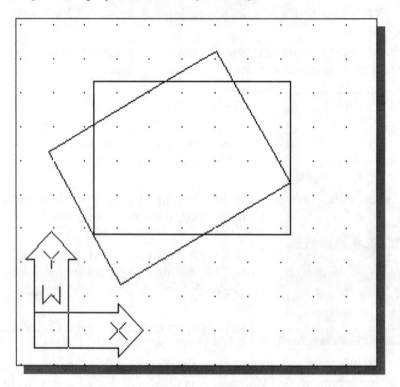

Setting up the Top View

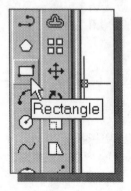

1. Select the **Rectangle** icon in the *Draw* toolbar. In the command prompt area, the message *"Specify first corner point or [Chamfer/Elevation/Fillet/Thickness/Width]:"* is displayed.

2. Move the cursor over the top left corner of the first rectangle we created. This will activate the *object tracking* alignment feature to the corner.

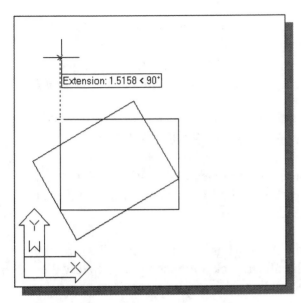

Extension: 1.5158 < 90°

3. Move the cursor upward to a location that is about 1.5" away from the reference point. (Read the *OTRACK* display on the screen.) Left-click once to place the first corner-point of the rectangle.

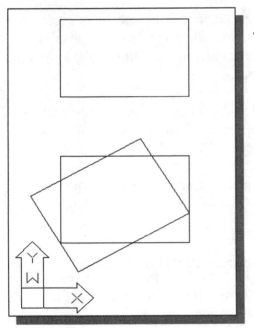

4. We will create a 3" X 2" rectangle. Enter **@3,2 [ENTER]**.

• We have created the outline of the top view of the *V-block* design.

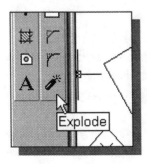

Explode

5. Pre-select the rectangle we just created by left-clicking any edge of the rectangle.

6. Select the **Explode** icon in the *Modify* toolbar.

• The top rectangle now consists of four separate line segments.

Using the *Offset* command

1. Select the **Offset** icon in the *Modify* toolbar. In the command prompt area, the message "*Specify offset distance or [Through]:*" is displayed.

2. In the command prompt area, enter: **0.2 [ENTER]**.

3. In the command prompt area, the message "*Select object to offset or <exit>:*" is displayed. Pick the **top horizontal line** of the top-view on the screen.

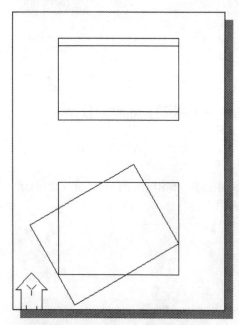

4. AutoCAD next asks us to identify the direction of the offset. Pick a location that is **below** the selected line.

5. In the command prompt area, the message "*Select object to offset or <exit>:*" is displayed. Pick the **bottom horizontal line** of the top-view on the screen.

6. AutoCAD next asks us to identify the direction of the offset. Pick a location that is above the selected line.

7. Inside the graphics window, **right-mouse-click** to end the *Offset* command.

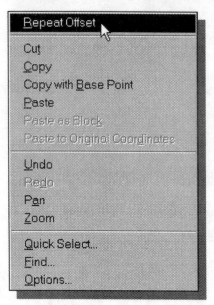

8. Inside the graphics window, **right-mouse-click** to bring up the popup option menu and select the **Repeat Offset** option.

• Notice in the popup menu, none of the GRIPS editing commands is displayed; the GRIPS editing commands are displayed only if objects are pre-selected.

9. In the command prompt area, the message *"Specify offset distance or [Through]:"* is displayed; enter: **0.75 [ENTER]**.

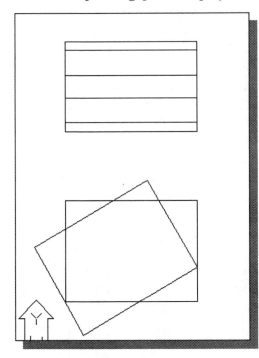

10. In the command prompt area, the message *"Select object to offset or <exit>:"* is displayed. Pick the **top horizontal line** of the top-view on the screen.

11. AutoCAD next asks us to identify the direction of the offset. Pick a location that is **below** the selected line.

12. In the command prompt area, the message *"Select object to offset or <exit>:"* is displayed. Pick the **bottom horizontal line** of the top-view on the screen.

13. AutoCAD next asks us to identify the direction of the offset. Pick a location that is above the selected line.

14. Inside the graphics window, **right-mouse-click** to end the *Offset* command.

* The four parallel lines will be used to construct the top v-cut feature and the two 0.75" **x** 30° cut features at the base of the v-block in the top view.

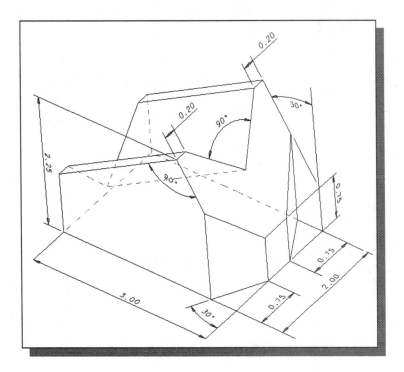

Creating object lines in the front view

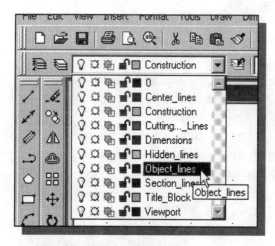

1. On the *Object Properties* toolbar, choose the *Layer Control* box with the left-mouse-button.

2. Move the cursor over the name of layer *Object_Lines*; the tool tip "*Object_Lines*" appears.

3. **Left-mouse-click once** and layer *Object_Lines* is set as the *Current Layer*.

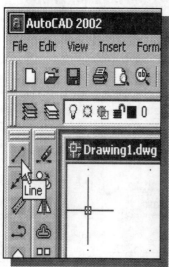

4. Select the **Line** command icon in the *Draw* toolbar. In the command prompt area, the message "*_line Specify first point:*" is displayed.

5. Pick the **lower-left corner** of the bottom horizontal line in the front-view as the starting point of the line segments.

6. Pick the **lower-right corner** of the bottom horizontal line in the front-view as the second point.

7. Select the **third** and **fourth** points as shown in the below figure.

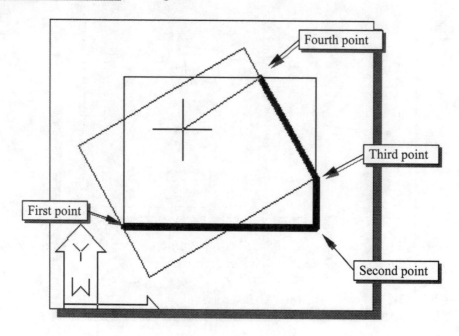

Setting the POLAR TRACKING option

1. In the *Status Bar* area, turn *ON* the *POLAR* option.

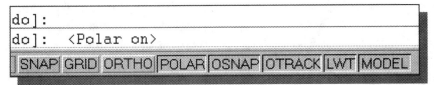

- Note that the *POLAR* option is one of the *AutoCAD AutoTrack^{TM}* features. The *AutoTrack* features include two tracking options: polar tracking and object snap tracking. When the *POLAR* option is turned on, alignment markers are displayed to help us create objects at precise positions and angles. A quick way to change the settings of the *AutoTrack* feature is to use the option menu.

2. Move the cursor on top of the *POLAR* option in the *Status Bar* area.

3. Click once with the **right-mouse-button** to bring up the option menu.

4. Select **Settings** in the option menu as shown in the figure.

5. In the *Drafting Settings* dialogue box, set the *Increment angle* to **30** as shown in the figure below.

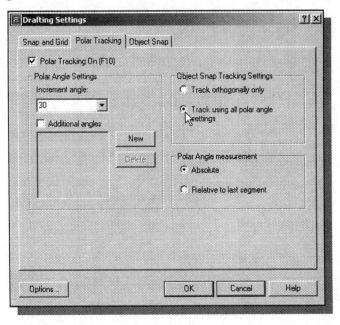

6. Under the *Object Snap Tracking Settings* option, turn *ON* the ***Track using all polar angle settings*** as shown in the figure above.

7. Click **OK** to accept the modified settings.

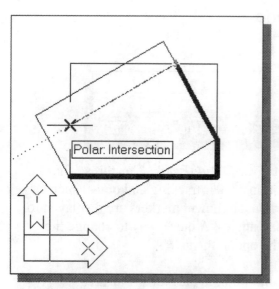

8. Move the cursor near the left-vertical line as shown and notice that *AutoCAD AutoTrack* automatically snaps the cursor to the intersection point and displays the alignment marker as shown.

➢ In the following steps, we will illustrate the use of different POLAR settings to achieve the same result.

9. Click once with the **right-mouse-button** on the *POLAR* option in the *Status Bar* area to bring up the option menu.

10. Select **Settings** in the option menu as shown in the figure.

11. In the *Drafting Settings* dialogue box, set the *Increment angle* to **90** as shown in the below figure.

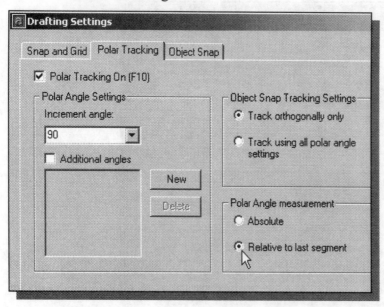

12. Under the *Object Snap Tracking Settings* option, turn **OFF** the ***Track orthogonally only*** as shown in the figure.

13. Under the *Object Snap Tracking Settings* option, turn **ON** the ***Relative to last segment*** option as shown in the figure above.

14. Click **OK** to accept the modified settings.

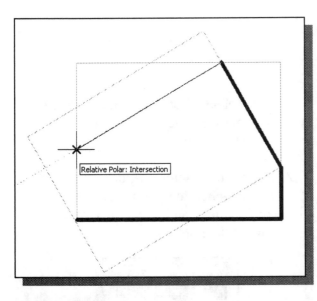

15. Move the cursor near the left vertical line and notice the *AutoTrack* feature automatically snaps the cursor to the intersection point and displays the alignment marker as shown.

➢ On your own, experiment with changing the settings to achieve the same *SNAP/POLAR* results.

16. Left-click at the intersection point as shown.

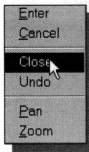

17. Inside the graphics window, right-mouse-click once to bring up the popup menu.

18. Pick the **Close** option in the popup menu. AutoCAD will create a line connecting the last point to the first point of the line sequence.

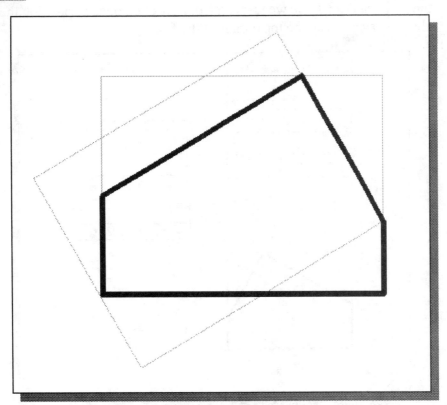

Setting up an auxiliary view

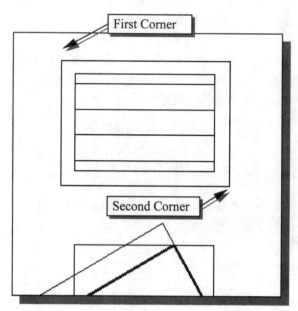

First Corner

Second Corner

1. **Pre-select** all objects in the top-view by enclosing the objects inside a selection window.

2. Inside the graphics window, **right-mouse-click** to bring up the popup option menu and select the **Copy Selection** option.

3. In the command prompt area, the message "*Specify base point or displacement, or [Multiple]:*" is displayed. Pick the **lower left corner** of the top-view as the base point.

4. Using the *AutoTrack* feature, place the copy of the top-view by aligning it to the inclined object line we just created. Left-click once to position the copy about 2" away from the top corner of the front-view.

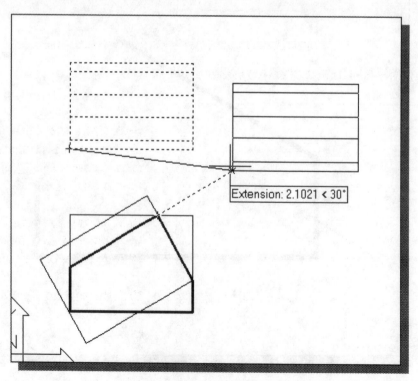

Extension: 2.1021 < 30°

Aligning the auxiliary view to the front view

1. **Pre-select** all objects in the auxiliary-view by enclosing the objects inside a selection window.

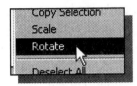

2. Inside the graphics window, **right-mouse-click** to bring up the popup option menu and select the **Rotate** option.

3. In the command prompt area, the message *"Specify base point:"* is displayed. Pick the **bottom-left corner** of the auxiliary-view as the base point.

4. In the command prompt area, the message *"Specify the rotation angle or [Reference]:"* is displayed. Enter: **-60 [ENTER]**.

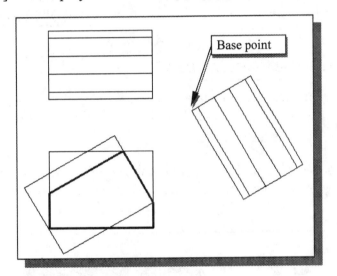

Creating the V-cut in the auxiliary view

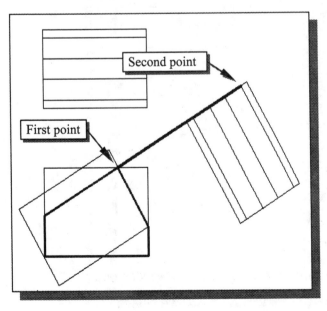

1. Select the **Line** icon in the *Draw* toolbar. In the command prompt area, the message *"_line Specify first point:"* is displayed.

2. Pick the **top corner** of the inclined object line in the front-view as the starting point of the line segments.

3. Pick the **second top end point** in the auxiliary-view as the second point.

4. Inside the graphics window, **right-mouse-click** and select **Enter** to end the *Line* command.

5. Pre-select the line we just created.

6. Inside the graphics window, **right-mouse-click** to bring up the popup option menu and select the **Rotate** option.

7. In the command prompt area, the message "*Specify base point:*" is displayed. Pick the top-right endpoint of the line as the base point.

8. In the command prompt area, the message "*Specify the rotation angle or [Reference]:*" is displayed. Enter: **45 [ENTER]**.

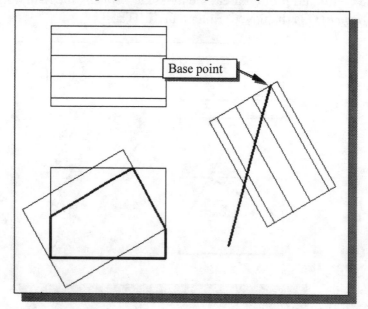

9. On your own, repeat the above steps and create the other line as shown.

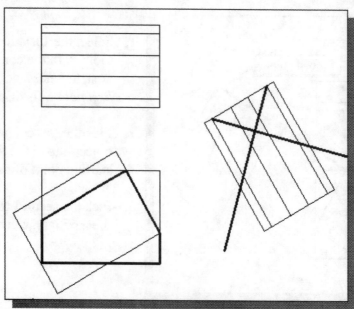

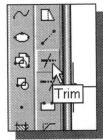

10. Select the **Trim** command icon in the *Modify* toolbar. In the command prompt area, the message *"Select boundary edges... Select objects:"* is displayed.

11. Pick the two inclined lines we just created in the auxiliary-view as the *boundary edges*.

12. Inside the graphics window, **right-mouse-click** to proceed with the *Trim* command. The message *"Select object to trim or [Project/Edge/Undo]:"* is displayed in the command prompt area.

13. Pick the two lower endpoints of the two inclined lines to remove the unwanted portions.

14. Inside the graphics window, **right-mouse-click** to activate the option menu and select **Enter** with the left-mouse-button to end the *Trim* command.

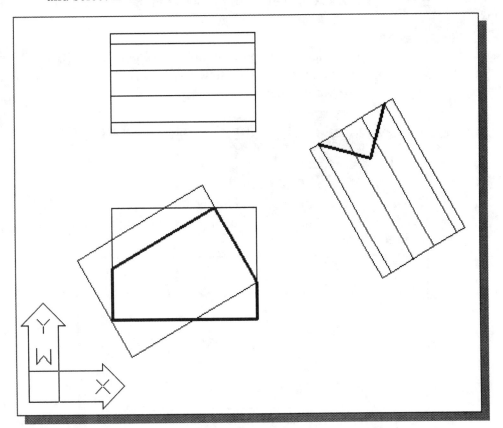

➢ The V-cut is shown at its true size and shape only in the auxiliary-view. It is therefore necessary to create the V-cut in the auxiliary-view. Now that we have constructed the feature in the auxiliary-view, we can use projection lines to transfer the feature to the front-view and top-view.

Creating the V-cut in the front-view and top-view

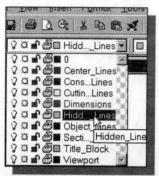

1. On the *Object Properties* toolbar, choose the *Layer Control* box with the left-mouse-button.

2. Move the cursor over the name of layer ***Hidden_Lines***; the tool tip *"Hidden_Lines"* appears.

3. **Left-mouse-click once** and layer *Hidden_Lines* is set as the *Current Layer*.

4. Select the ***Line*** command icon in the *Draw* toolbar. In the command prompt area, the message "*_line Specify first point:*" is displayed.

5. Pick the **vertex** of the V-cut in the *auxiliary view* as the first point of the line.

6. Inside the graphics window, hold down the **[SHIFT]** key and **right-mouse-click** once to bring up the *Object Snap* shortcut menu.

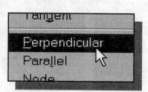

7. Select the **Perpendicular** option in popup window.

8. Move the cursor to the front-view and notice the perpendicular symbol appears at different locations. Select the intersection point on the inclined line as shown in the figure below.

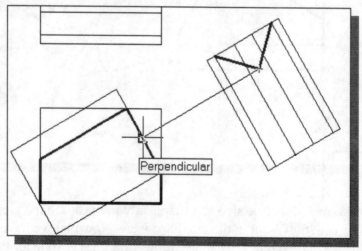

9. Inside the graphics window, **right-mouse-click** to activate the option menu and select **Enter** with the left-mouse-button to end the *Line* command.

10. On your own, use the **Trim** and **Extend** commands to adjust the hidden lines in the front view.

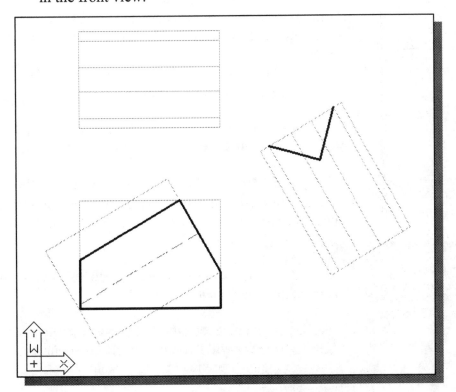

➤ On your own, first create the two construction lines and then construct the V-cut feature in the top-view. Use the **Trim** and **Extend** commands to assist the construction.

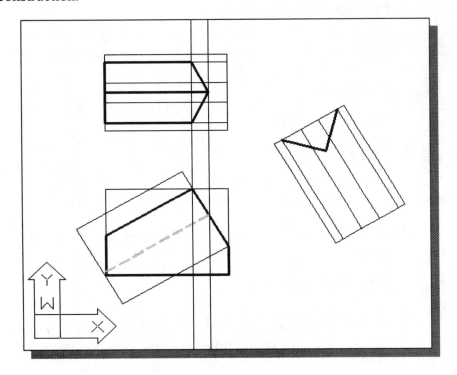

Setting the POLAR TRACKING option

1. Move the cursor to the *Status Bar* area, over the *POLAR* option button.

2. **Right-mouse-click once** to bring up a popup option menu.

3. Select the **Settings** option by clicking once with the left-mouse-button. This is the shortcut to bring up the *Drafting Settings* dialog box.

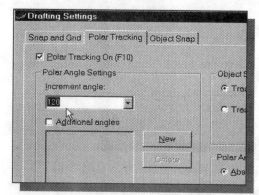

4. In the *Drafting Settings* dialog box, set the *Increment angle* to **120**.

➤ Notice the other settings that are available. We will use the absolute polar angle measurement for this example.

5. Click on the **OK** button to accept the settings.

Completing the top-view

1. Click on the **Zoom Realtime** icon in the *Standard* toolbar area.

2. Move the cursor near the center of the graphics window.

3. **Push and hold down the left-mouse-button**, then move upward to enlarge the current display scale factor. (Press the [**Esc**] key to exit the command.)

4. Use the **Pan Realtime** option to reposition the display so that we can work on the top-view of the V-block.

5. Select the **Line** icon in the *Draw* toolbar.

6. In the command prompt area, the message "*_line Specify first point:*" is displayed. Pick the **right endpoint** of the third horizontal line in the top-view as the starting point of the line segments.

7. Move the cursor toward the top horizontal line and observe the *AutoTracking* markers over different locations.

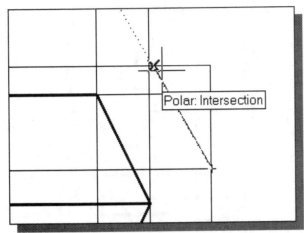

8. **Left-click** at the intersection of the polar tracking and the top-horizontal line as shown. Do not select the intersection between the top horizontal line and the vertical line. (Use the *Zoom Realtime* command to zoom-in further if necessary.)

9. Inside the graphics window, **right-mouse-click** and select **Enter** to end the *Line* command.

10. Repeat the above steps and create the other inclined line in the top-view.

➢ On your own, complete the top-view by adding all the necessary object lines in the top-view. Use the *Trim* and *Extend* commands to assist the construction.

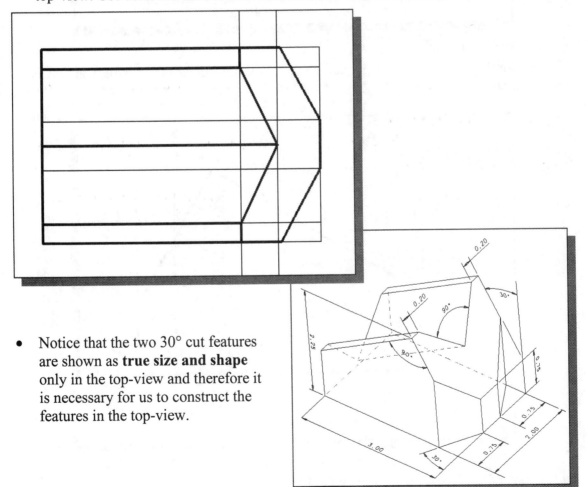

- Notice that the two 30° cut features are shown as **true size and shape** only in the top-view and therefore it is necessary for us to construct the features in the top-view.

➢ On your own, create the **vertical construction line** through the corner of the 30° cut as shown.

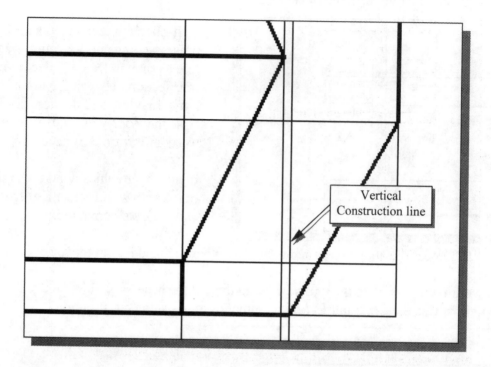

11. Complete the front-view by adding the object line along the construction line as shown.

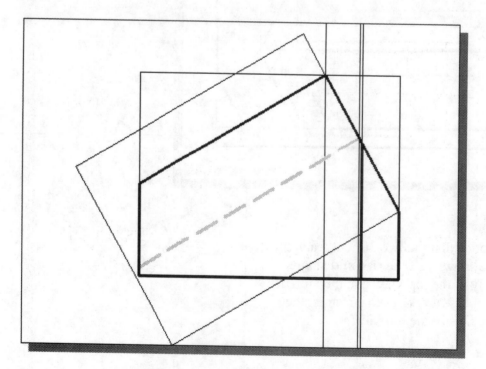

➢ On your own, complete the views by adding all the necessary object lines in the views.

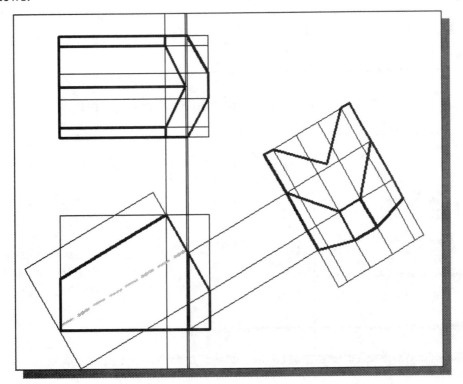

➢ Complete the drawing by adding the proper dimensions.

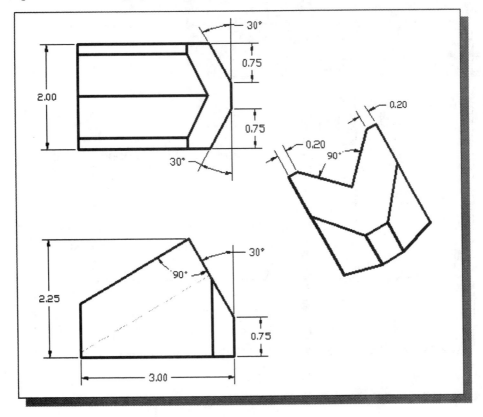

Edit the Plot Style table

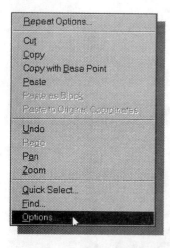

1. Inside the graphics window, **right-mouse-click** and select **Options** in the popup menu.

2. In the *Options* dialog box, select the **Plotting** tab.

   Notice we are using *acad.stb* as the *Default plot style table*.

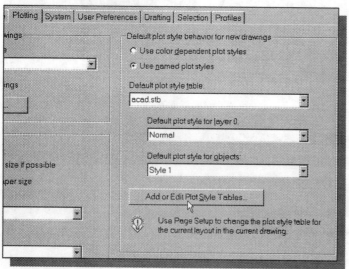

3. In the *Options* dialog box, click on the **Add or Edit Plot Style Tables** button.

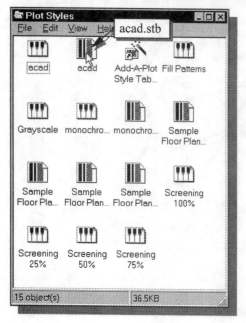

4. The *Plot Styles* folder appears on the screen.

5. Double-click the *acad.stb* icon with the left-mouse-button to open the plot style file.

6. In the *Plot Style Table Editor*, select the **Table View** tab.

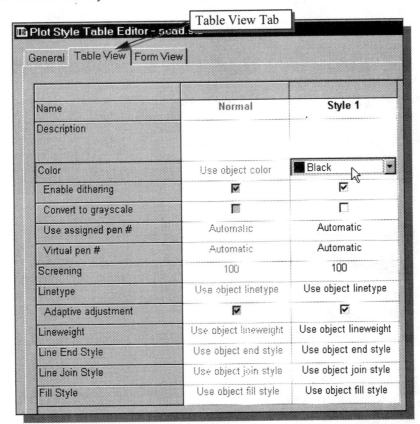

-   The *Plot Style Table Editor* displays the plot styles that are in the current plot style table. The **Table View** and **Form View** tabs provide two methods to modify the existing plot style settings. Both tabs list all of the plot styles in the plot style table and their settings. In general, the **Table View** tab is more convenient if there is only a small number of plot styles. We can modify plot style color, screening, linetype, lineweight, and other settings. The first plot style in a named plot style table is *Normal* and represents an object's default properties (no plot style applied). We cannot modify or delete the *Normal* style.

7. Change the *Color* setting for *Style 1* to **Black**, so that all layers using this plot style will print using black.

8. Pick the **Save&Close** button to accept the settings and exit the *Plot Style Table Editor*.

➢ On your own, print out a copy of the *V-block* drawing using the modified plot style table.

Questions:

1. What is an auxiliary view and why would it be important?

2. When is a line viewed as a point? How can a line be shown in true length?

3. What is a GRIP? What are the advantages of using the GRIPS?

4. List three GRIPS editing commands you have used in the tutorial.

5. Identify the following commands:

(a)

(b)

(c)

(d)

Exercises:

1.

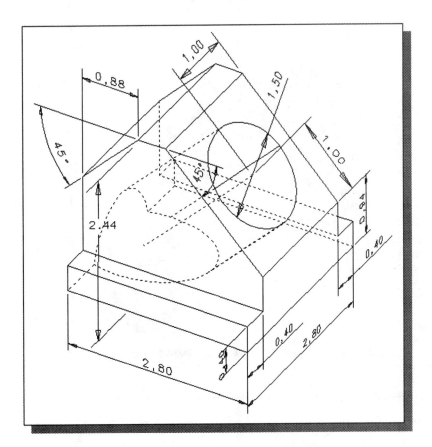

2.

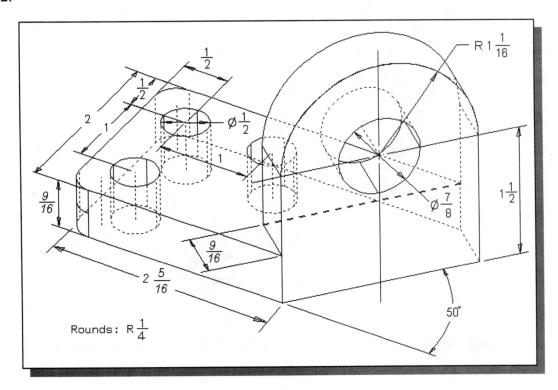

3.

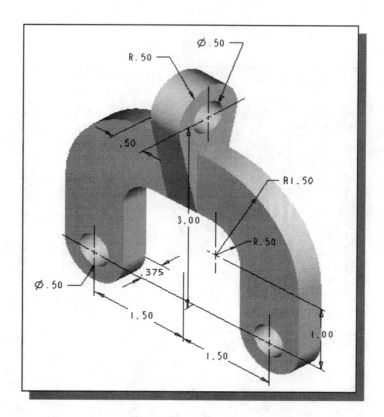

4.

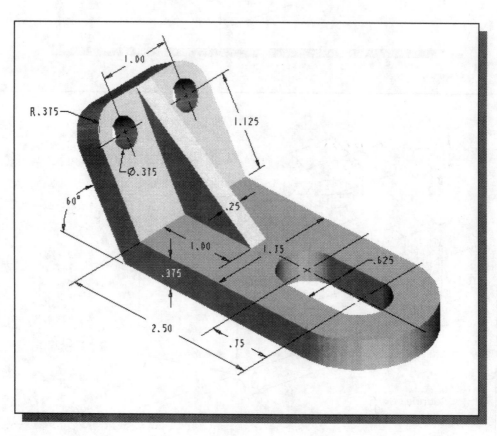

Lesson 9
Section Views

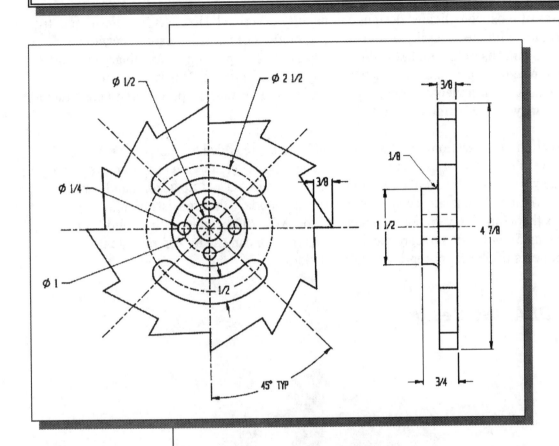

Learning Objectives

♦ **Use CAD methods to create Section Views.**
♦ **Use the Object Snap Shortcut options.**
♦ **Change the Linetype Scale property.**
♦ **Stretch and move objects with GRIPS.**
♦ **Create cutting plane lines.**
♦ **Use the HATCH command.**

Introduction

In the previous lessons, we have explored the basic CAD methods of creating orthographic views. By carefully selecting a limited number of views, the external features of most complicated designs can be fully described. However, we are frequently confronted with the necessity of showing the interiors of parts that cannot be shown clearly by means of hidden lines. We accomplish this by passing an imaginary cutting plane through the part and creating a cutaway view of the part. This type of view is known as a **section view**. In this lesson, we will demonstrate the procedure to construct a section view using **AutoCAD® 2002**.

In a section view, section lines, or cross-hatch lines, are added to indicate the surfaces that are cut by the imaginary cutting plane. The type of section line used to represent a surface varies according to the type of material. AutoCAD's *Hatch* command can be used to fill a pattern inside an area. We define a boundary that consists of an object or objects that completely enclose the area. **AutoCAD® 2002** comes with a solid fill and more than 50 industry-standard hatch patterns that we can use to differentiate the components of objects or represent object materials.

The *BEARING* Design

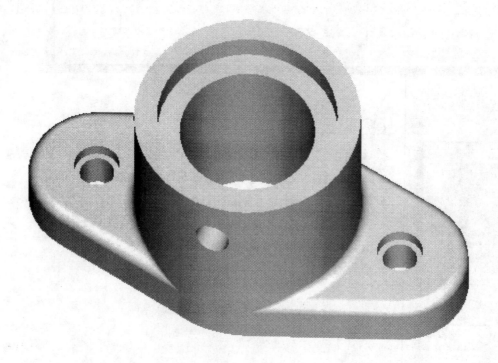

Starting Up AutoCAD 2000

1. Select the **AutoCAD 2002** option on the *Program* menu or select the **AutoCAD 2002** icon on the *Desktop*.

2. In the *AutoCAD Today* startup dialog box, select the **Template** option.

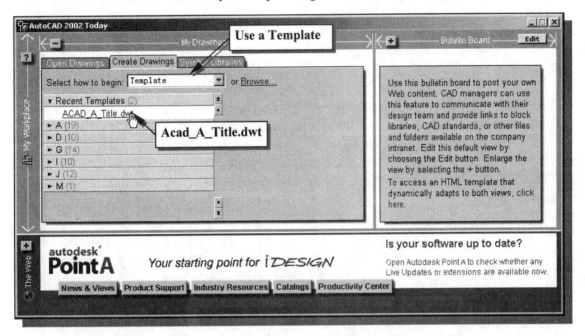

3. Select the *Acad_A_Title* template file from the list of template files. If the template file is not listed, click on the **Browse** button to locate and proceed to open a new drawing file.

4. Pick **Layers** in the *Object Properties* toolbar.

5. Examine the layer property settings in the *Layer Properties Manager* dialog box.

6. Click on the **OK** button to exit the *Layer Properties Manager* dialog box.

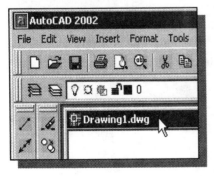

7. Switch to the *Drawing1* window by left-clicking once in the title area of the window.

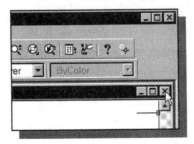

8. Close the window by clicking the **Close** icon located at the upper-right-corner of the *Drawing1* window.

The *Bearing* Example

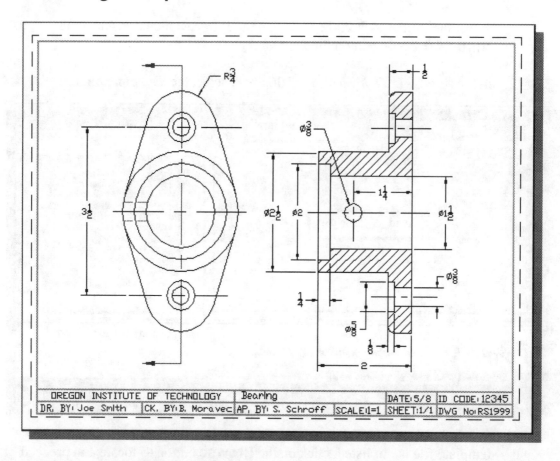

Setting up the principal views

1. In the *Status Bar* area, reset the options and turn **ON** the *OSNAP, OTRACK, LWT*, and *MODEL* options.

- We will first create construction lines for the front-view.

2. Select the **Construction Line** icon in the *Draw* toolbar.

3. In the command prompt area, the message "_xline Specify a point or [Hor/Ver/Ang/Bisect/Offset]:" is displayed. On your own, create a vertical line and a horizontal line as shown in the figure below. These lines will be used as the references for the circular features of the design.

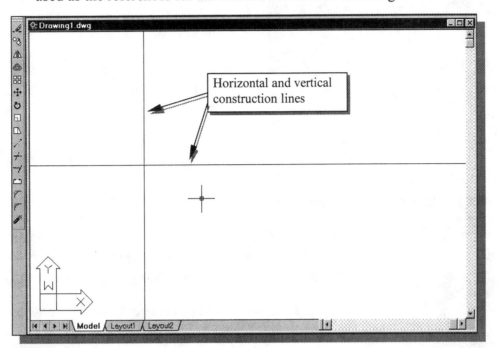

4. Click on the **Offset** icon in the *Modify* toolbar. In the command prompt area, the message "*Specify offset distance or [Through]:*" is displayed.

5. In the command prompt area, enter: **1.75 [ENTER]**.

6. In the command prompt area, the message "*Select object to offset or <exit>:*" is displayed. Pick the **horizontal line** on the screen.

7. AutoCAD next expects us to identify the direction of the offset. Pick a location that is above the selected line.

8. We will also create a line that is below the original horizontal line at 1.75. Pick the original **horizontal line** on the screen.

9. Pick a location that is below the selected line.

10. Inside the graphics window, **right-mouse-click** to end the *Offset* command.

Creating object lines in the front-view

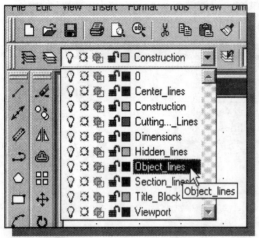

1. On the *Object Properties* toolbar, choose the **Layer Control** box with the left-mouse-button.

2. Move the cursor over the name of layer **Object_Lines**; the tool tip "*Object_Lines*" appears.

3. **Left-mouse-click once** and layer *Object_Lines* is set as the *Current Layer*.

4. Click on the **Circle** icon in the *Draw* toolbar. In the command prompt area, the message "*Specify center point for circle or [3P/2P/Ttr (tan tan radius)]:*" is displayed.

5. Pick the center intersection point as the center of the circle.

6. In the command prompt area, the message "*Specify radius of circle or [Diameter]:*" is displayed. Enter: **1.25 [ENTER]**.

7. Repeat the **Circle** command and create the two diameter 1.5 circles as shown.

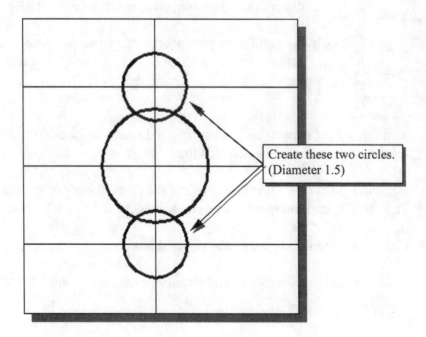

Create these two circles.
(Diameter 1.5)

8. Select the **Line** command icon in the *Draw* toolbar. In the command prompt area, the message "*_line Specify first point:*" is displayed.

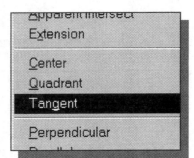

9. Inside the graphics window, hold down the **[SHIFT]** key and **right-mouse-click** once to bring up the *Object Snap* shortcut menu.

10. Select the **Tangent** option in popup window. Move the cursor near the circles and notice the *Tangent* marker appears at different locations.

- The *Tangent* option enables us to create tangent lines; **select objects by clicking near the expected tangency locations**.

11. Pick the top circle by clicking on the upper-right section of the circle.

12. In the command prompt area, the message "*Specify the next point or [Undo]:*" is displayed. Inside the graphics window, hold down the **[SHIFT]** key and **right-mouse-click** once to bring up the *Object Snap* shortcut menu.

13. Select the **Tangent** option in the popup menu.

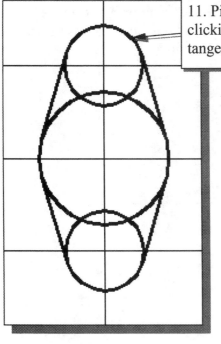

11. Pick the top circle by clicking near the expected tangency location.

14. Pick the center circle by clicking on the right side of the circle. A line tangent to the two circles appears on the screen.

15. Inside the graphics window, **right-mouse-click** and select **Enter** to end the *Line* command.

16. Repeat the *Line* command and create the four tangent lines as shown.

Editing the circles

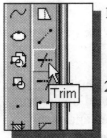

1. Select the **Trim** icon in the *Modify* toolbar. In the command prompt area, the message "*Select boundary edges... Select objects:*" is displayed.

2. Pick the four lines we just created as the *boundary edges*.

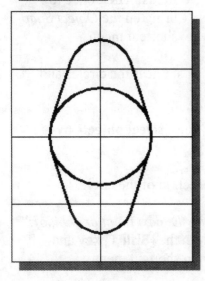

3. Inside the graphics window, **right-mouse-click** to proceed with the *Trim* command. The message "*Select object to trim or [Project/Edge/Undo]:*" is displayed in the command prompt area.

4. *Trim* the unwanted portions of the top and bottom circles and complete the outline of the front-view as shown.

5. Inside the graphics window, **right-mouse-click** to activate the option menu and select **Enter** with the left-mouse-button to end the *Trim* command.

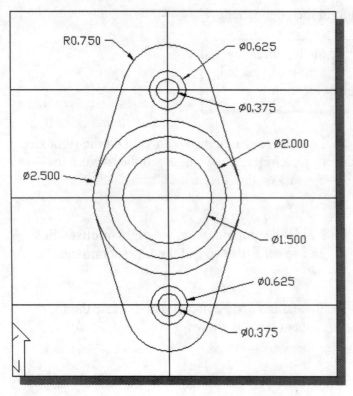

➢ On your own, create the additional circles as shown.

Setting up the side-view

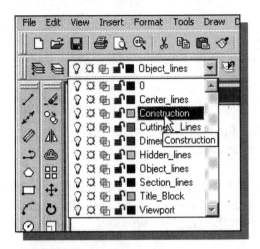

1. In the *Layer Control* box, set layer *Construction_Lines* as the *Current Layer*.

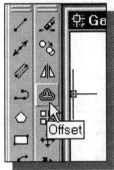

2. Select the **Offset** icon in the *Modify* toolbar. In the command prompt area, the message "*Specify offset distance or [Through]:*" is displayed.

3. In the command prompt area, enter: **5.0 [ENTER]**.

4. In the command prompt area, the message "*Select object to offset or <exit>:*" is displayed. Pick the **vertical line** on the screen.

5. AutoCAD next expects us to identify the direction of the offset. Pick a location that is toward the right side of the selected line.

6. Inside the graphics window, **right-mouse-click** to end the *Offset* command.

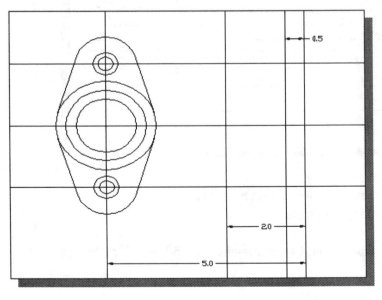

> On your own, repeat the *Offset* command and create two additional lines parallel to the line we just created as shown (distances of 0.5 and 2.0).

7. Select the **Construction Line** icon in the *Draw* toolbar. In the command prompt area, the message "*_xline Specify a point or [Hor/Ver/Ang/Bisect/Offset]:*" is displayed.

8. Inside the graphics window, **right-mouse-click** to bring up the popup menu.

9. Select the **Hor** (horizontal) option in the popup menu.

    ➢ The **Horizontal** option enables us to create a horizontal line by specifying one point in the graphics window.

10. Create **projection lines** by clicking at the intersections between the vertical line and the circles (and arcs) in the front-view.

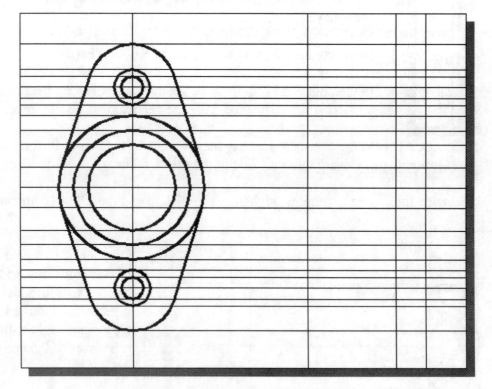

11. Also create two horizontal projection lines that pass through the two tangency-points on the Ø2.5 circle.

12. Inside the graphics window, **right-mouse-click** to end the *Construction Line* command.

> On your own, create object lines to show the outline of the side view.

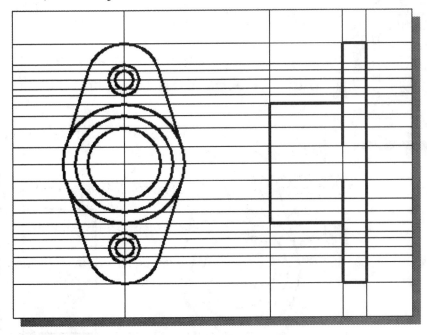

Adding hidden lines in the side-view

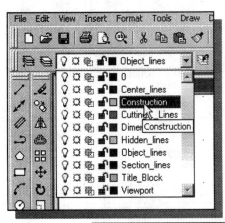

1. In the *Layer Control* box, set layer *Construction_Lines* as the *Current Layer*.

2. Use the **Offset** command and create the two additional vertical lines, for the counter-bore features, as shown.

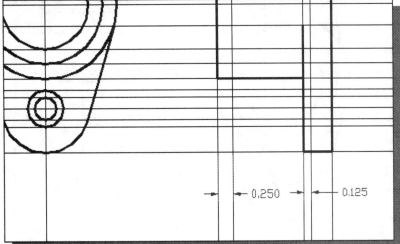

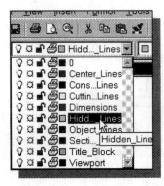

3. Set layer **Hidden_Lines** as the *Current Layer* in the *Layer Control* box.

4. Use the **Line** command and create the hidden lines as shown.

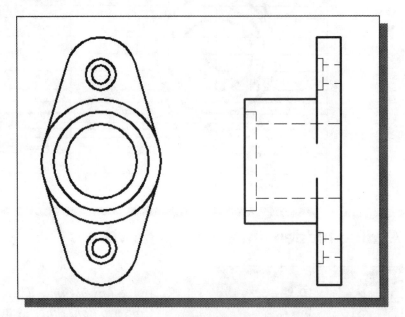

➤ On your own, complete the views by adding the side-drill, the centerlines, and the rounded corners as shown.

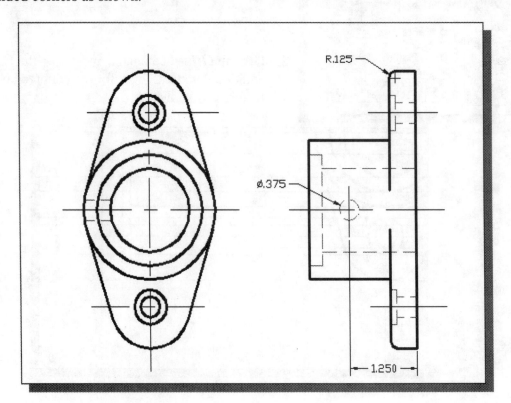

Changing the *Linetype Scale* property

❖ Looking at the side-drill feature and the centerlines we just created, not all of the lengths of the dash-dot linetypes appeared properly on the screen. The appearances of the dash-dot linetypes can be adjusted by modifying the ***Linetype Scale*** setting, which can be found under the *Object Property* option.

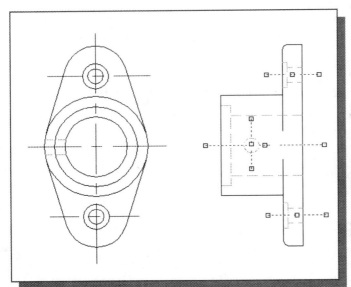

1. **Pre-select** the objects in the side-view as shown (four lines and one circle).

2. In the *Standard* toolbar, select the **Properties** icon.

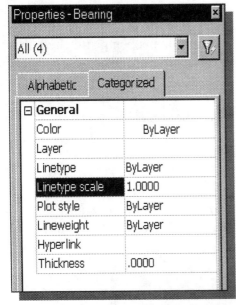

3. In the *Properties* dialog box, notice the default *Linetype scale* is 1.00.

4. Left-click on ***Linetype scale*** in the list and enter a new value: **0.5 [ENTER]**.

5. Click on the **[X]** button to exit the *Properties* dialog box.

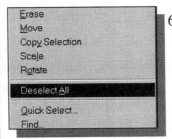

6. Inside the graphics window, **right-mouse-click** and select **Deselect All**.

➤ The appearances of the dash-dot linetypes of the selected objects are adjusted to half-size of the other objects. Keep in mind that the dash-dot linetypes may appear differently on paper, depending on the type of printer/plotter being used. You may want to do more adjustments after examining a printed/plotted copy of the drawing. It is also more common to adjust the *Linetype Scale* for all objects of the same linetype to maintain a consistent presentation of the drawing.

Stretching and moving objects with *GRIPS*

We can usually *stretch* an object by moving selected grips to new locations. Some grips will not stretch the object but will move the object. This is true of grips on text objects, blocks, midpoints of lines, centers of circles, centers of ellipses, and point objects.

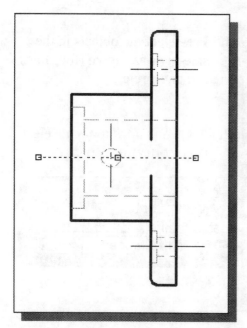

1. **Pre-select** the horizontal centerline that goes through the center of the part as shown.

2. Select the **right grip** by left-clicking once on the grip. Notice the grip is highlighted.

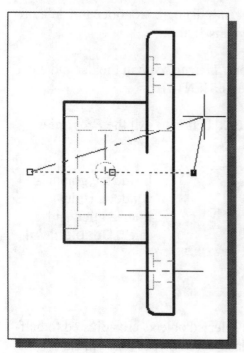

3. Move the cursor inside the graphics window and notice the center line is being stretched; the base point is attached to the cursor.

4. Pick a location on the screen to stretch the centerline.

5. Click on the **Undo** icon in the *Standard* toolbar area to undo the stretch we just did.

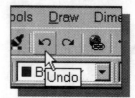

➤ On your own, experiment with moving the center grip of the centerline.

Drawing a cutting plane line

- Most section views require a cutting plane line to indicate the location on which the object is cut.

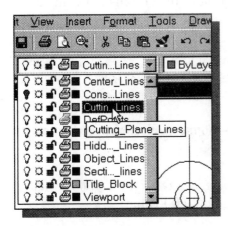

1. In the *Layer Control* box, turn *OFF* the *Construction_Lines* layer and set layer ***Cutting_Plane_Lines*** as the *Current Layer*.

2. Use the ***Line*** command and create the vertical cutting plane line aligned to the vertical centerline of the front-view.

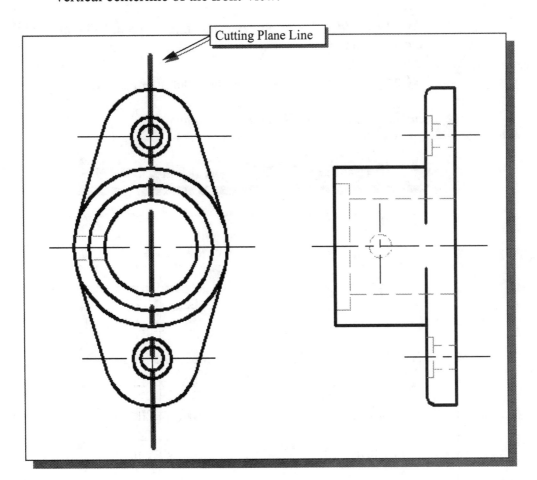

Cutting Plane Line

3. In the pull-down menus, select:

   [Dimension] → [Leader]

4. Move the cursor over the top endpoint of the cutting plane line to activate the *AutoTracking* option, and then select a point that is toward the left of the cutting plane line.

5. Pick the top endpoint of the cutting plane line to create a horizontal arrow.

6. Inside the graphics window, **right-mouse-click** to proceed with the *Leader* command.

7. In the command prompt area, the message "*Specify Text height <0.000>:*" is displayed. **Right-mouse-click** to accept the default **0.00** value.

8. In the command prompt area, the message "*Enter first line of annotation text <Mtext>:*" is displayed. **Right-mouse-click** to continue.

9. The *Multiline Text Editor* dialog box appears on the screen. Click on the **OK** button to close the dialog box.

10. Repeat the ***Leader*** command and create the other arrow as shown.

11. In the *Status Bar* area, turn **OFF** the *LWT* option.

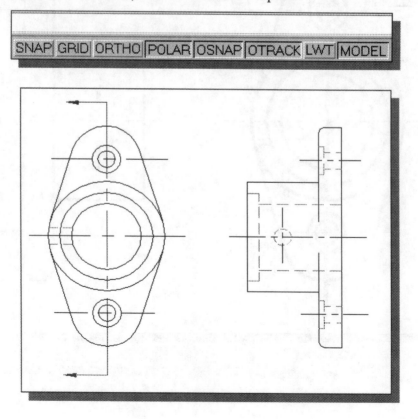

Converting the side-view into a section view

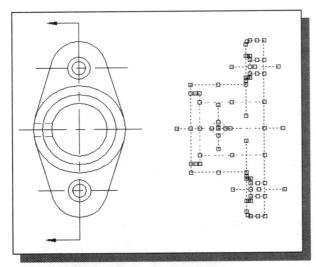

1. **Pre-select** all the objects in the side-view by using a selection window.

2. Inside the graphics window, **right-mouse-click** to bring up the popup option menu and select the **Quick Select** option.

❖ The *Quick Select* option enables us to quickly select multiple objects by using varies *Filter* options.

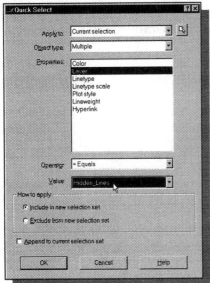

3. In the *Quick Select* dialog box, select *Layer* from the *Properties* list.

4. Set the *Value* box to *Hidden_Lines*.

5. In the *How to apply* section, confirm the *Include in new selection set* option is selected.

6. Click on the **OK** button to accept the settings.

❖ AutoCAD will now **filter out** objects that are not on layer *Hidden_lines*.

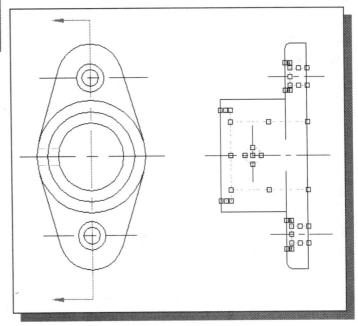

7. On the *Object Properties* toolbar, choose the *Layer Control* box with the left-mouse-button.

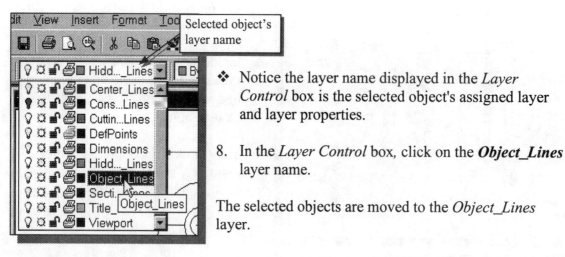

❖ Notice the layer name displayed in the *Layer Control* box is the selected object's assigned layer and layer properties.

8. In the *Layer Control* box, click on the **Object_Lines** layer name.

The selected objects are moved to the *Object_Lines* layer.

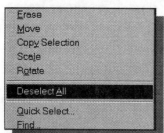

9. Inside the graphics window, **right-mouse-click** and select **Deselect All**.

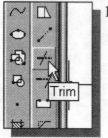

10. Use the **Trim** command and modify the side-view as shown.

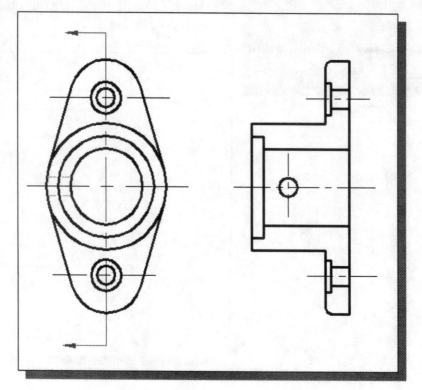

Adding section lines

1. In the *Layer Control* box, set layer **Section_Lines** as the *Current Layer*.

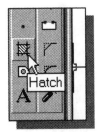

2. Select the **Hatch** icon in the *Draw* toolbar. The *Boundary Hatch* dialog box appears on the screen.

- We will use the *ANSI31* standard hatch pattern and create an associative hatch, which means the hatch is updated automatically if the boundaries are modified.

❖ We can define a boundary by **Selecting Objects** or **Picking Points**. The **Pick Points** option is usually the easier and faster way to define boundaries. We specify locations inside the region to be crosshatched and AutoCAD will automatically derive the boundary definition from the location of the specified point.

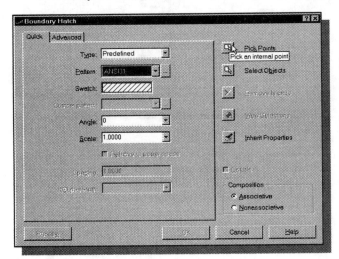

3. Click on the **Pick Points** icon.

4. In the command prompt area, the message "*Select internal point:*" is displayed.

5. **Left-click** inside the four regions as shown.

6. Inside the graphics window, **right-mouse-click** to bring up the popup menu and select **ENTER** to continue with the *Hatch* command.

7. Click on the **OK** button to close the *Boundary Hatch* dialog box.

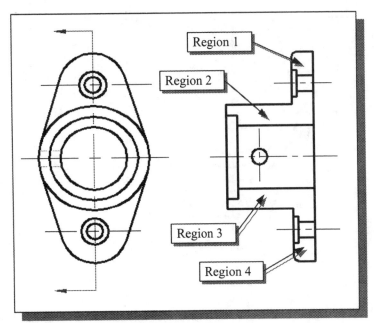

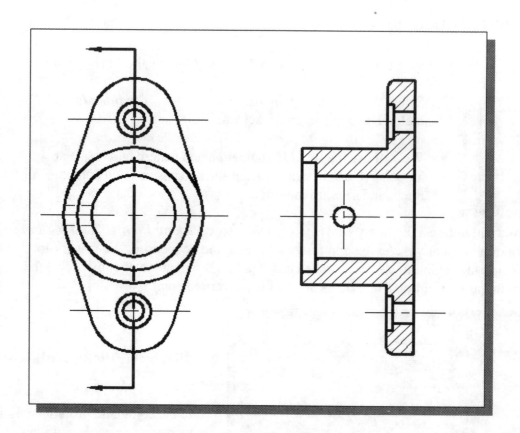

➤ Complete the drawing by adding the proper dimensions.

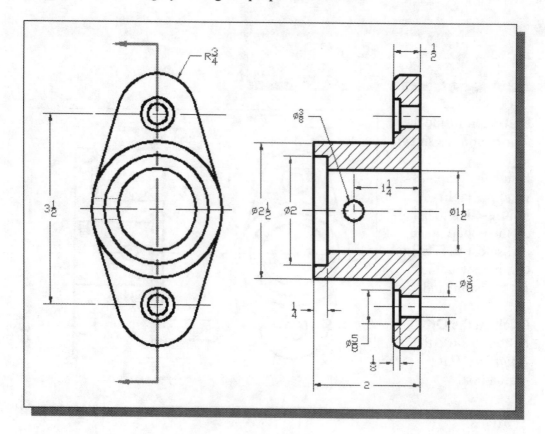

➢ On your own, create a drawing layout and print out the drawing.

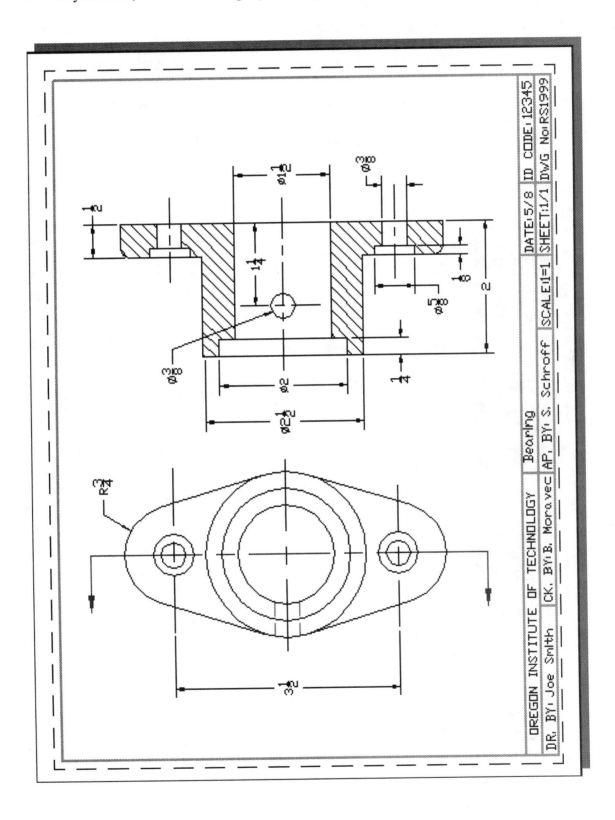

Questions:

1. When and why is a *section view* necessary?

2. Describe the general procedure to create a *section view* in **AutoCAD® 2002**.

3. In **AutoCAD® 2002**, can the angle and spacing of hatch patterns be altered?

4. Explain the concept of using a cutting plane line in a section view?

5. Identify the following commands:

(a)

(b)

(c)

(d)

Exercises:

1.

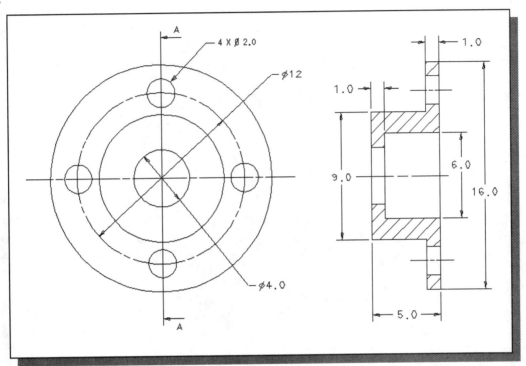

2.

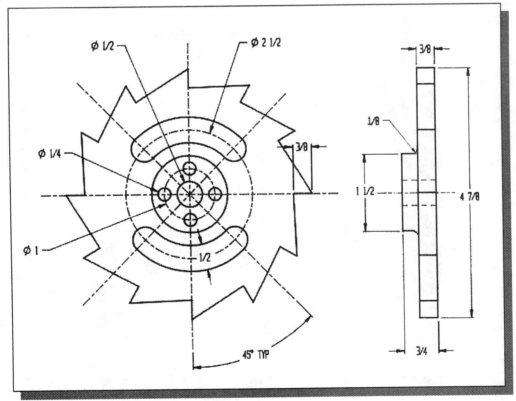

3.

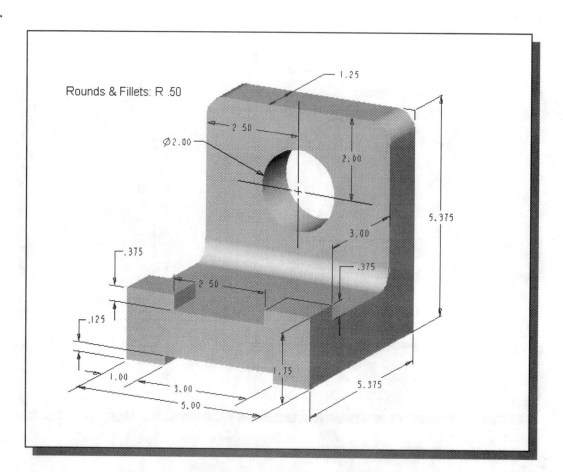

Rounds & Fillets: R .50

4.

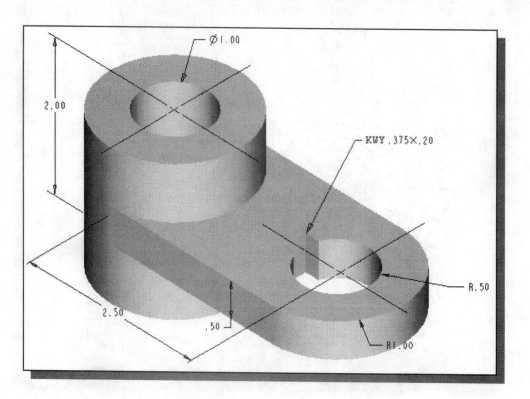

5.

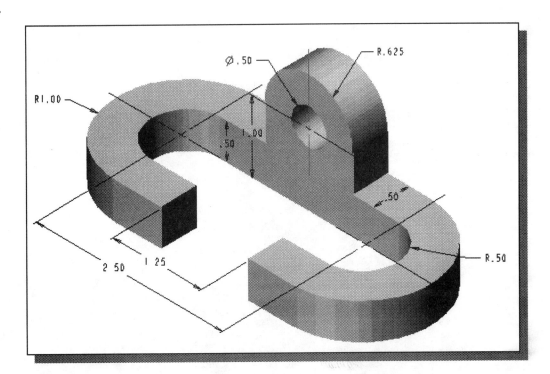

6.

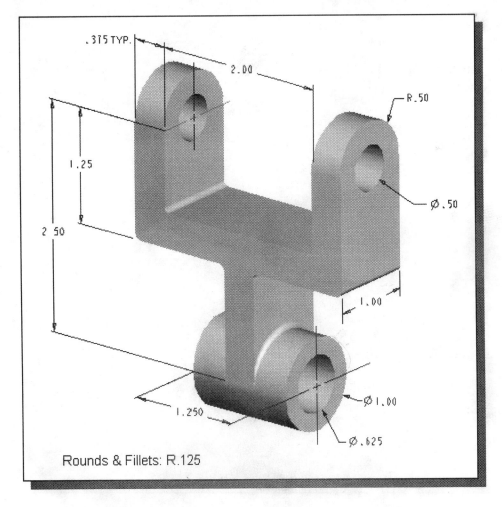

Rounds & Fillets: R.125

Notes:

Lesson 10
Assembly Drawings and Blocks

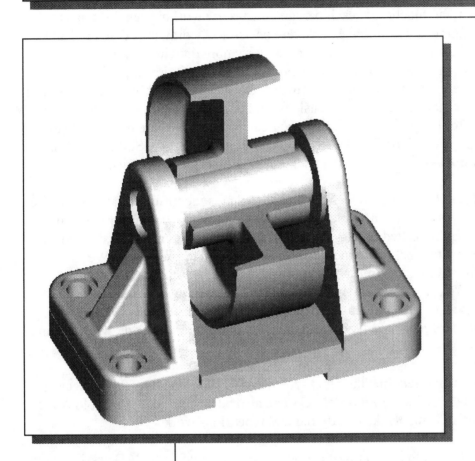

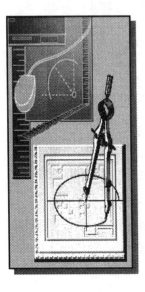

Learning Objectives

- ♦ **Create an Assembly Drawing from Part files.**
- ♦ **Using AutoCAD with the Internet.**
- ♦ **Load Multiple Drawings into a single AutoCAD session.**
- ♦ **Define a Block.**
- ♦ **Create multiple copies using BLOCKS.**
- ♦ **Copy and paste with the Windows Clipboard.**
- ♦ **Use the MOVE and ROTATE commands.**

Introduction

The term **assembly drawing** refers to the type of drawing in which the various parts of a design are shown in their relative positions in the finished product. Assembly drawings are used to represent the function of each part and the proper working relationships of the mating parts. Sectioning is used more extensively on assembly drawings than on detail drawings to show the relationship of various parts. Assembly drawings should not be overly detailed since precise information is provided on the detail drawings. In most cases dimensions are omitted on assembly drawings except for assembly dimensions such as important center distances, overall dimensions, and dimensions showing relationships between the parts. For the purpose of clarity, *subassembly drawings* are often made to give the information needed for the smaller units of a larger assembly. Several options are available in **AutoCAD® 2002** to assist us in creating assembly drawings.

In **AutoCAD® 2002**, a **block** is a collection of objects that is identified by a unique name and essentially behaves as if it is a single object. Using blocks can help us organize our design by associating the related objects into smaller units. We can insert, scale, and rotate multiple objects that belong to the same block with a single selection. We can insert the same block numerous times instead of re-creating the individual geometric objects each time. We can also import a block from a CAD file outside the current drawing. We can use blocks to build a standard library of frequently used symbols, components, or standard parts; the blocks can then be inserted into other drawings. Using blocks also helps us save disk space by storing all references to the same block as one block definition in the database. We can *explode* a block to separate its component objects, modify them, and redefine the block. **AutoCAD® 2002** updates all instances of that block based on the *block definition*. Blocks can also be nested, so that one block is a part of another block. Using blocks greatly reduces repetitious work.

In **AutoCAD® 2002**, we can load multiple drawings into a single AutoCAD session. This feature enables us to work with multiple drawings at the same time, and we can easily copy objects from one drawing to another by using the *Windows Clipboard*. Copying to and pasting from the *Clipboard* allow us to quickly assemble objects in different files and thus increase our productivity.

AutoCAD® 2002 also allows us to create a collaborative design environment, where files and resources can be shared through the Internet. We can open and save AutoCAD drawings to an Internet location, insert blocks by dragging drawings from a web site, and insert hyperlinks in drawings so that others can access related documents. To use the **AutoCAD® 2002** Internet features, *Microsoft Internet Explorer 5.0* (or a later version) and Internet or intranet connections are required.

In this lesson, we will demonstrate using the **AutoCAD® 2002** Internet features to access drawings through the Internet, as well as using blocks and the *Windows Clipboard* to create a subassembly drawing. We will use the bearing part that was created in the previous lesson.

The *Shaft Support* Subassembly

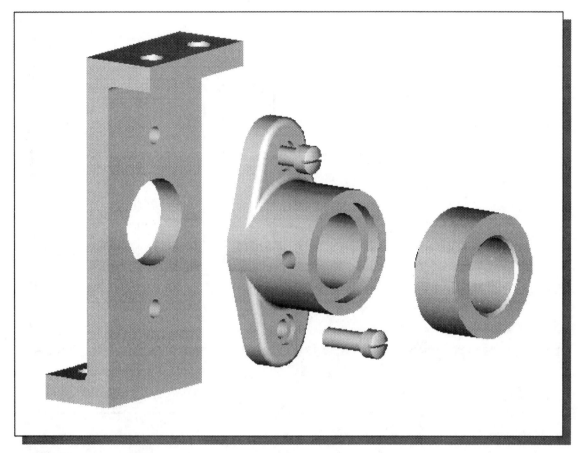

Additional parts

Besides the **Bearing**, we will need three additional parts: (1) **Cap-Screw**, (2) **Collar** and (3) **Base-Plate**. Create the collar and base-plate drawings as shown below, save the drawings as separate part files (*Collar*, *Base-Plate*). (Exit **AutoCAD® 2002** after you have created the files.)

(1) Cap-Screw
(We will open this drawing through the Internet.)

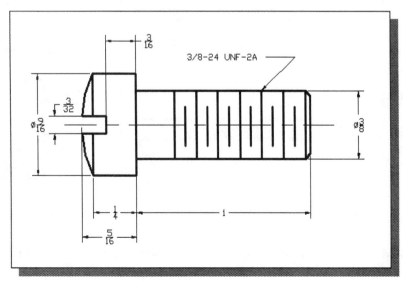

(2) *Collar*

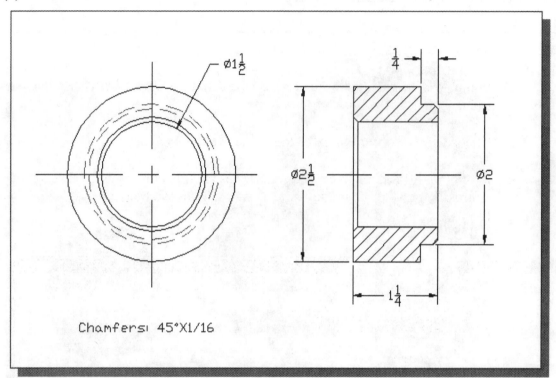

Chamfers: 45°X1/16

(3) *Base-Plate*

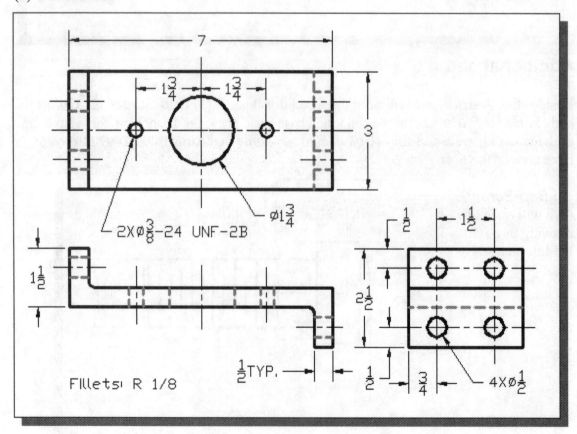

Starting Up AutoCAD 2002 and Loading Multiple Drawings

1. Select the **AutoCAD 2002** option on the *Program* menu or select the **AutoCAD 2002** icon on the *Desktop*.

2. In the *AutoCAD Today* startup dialog box, select the **Open Drawing** tab with a single click of the left-mouse-button.

3. Choose ***Most Recently Used*** as the *Select how to begin* option.

4. In the *File* list section, pick ***Bearing.dwg*** as the first drawing to be loaded. (If the file is not listed in the *File* list, use the **Browse** button to locate the file.)

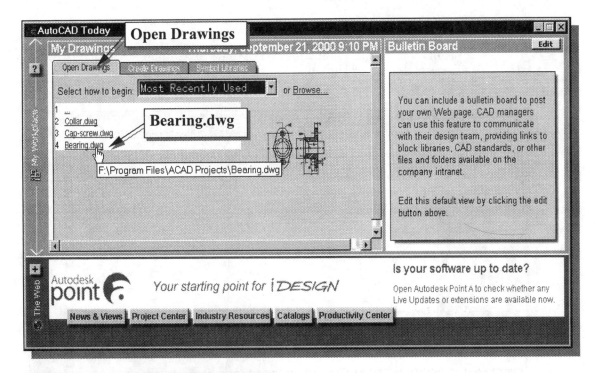

5. In the *AutoCAD Today* startup dialog box, pick ***Base-Plate.dwg*** as the second drawing to be loaded.

6. On your own, repeat the above steps and open the ***Collar.dwg*** file.

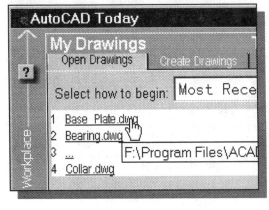

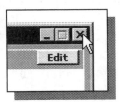

7. Close the *AutoCAD Today* dialog box by clicking the **[X]** icon.

Using AutoCAD with the Internet

- **AutoCAD® 2002** allows us to share files and resources through the Internet. Drawings can be placed and opened to an Internet location, insert blocks by dragging drawings from a web site, and insert hyperlinks in drawings so that others can access related documents. Note that to use the **AutoCAD® 2002** Internet features, *Microsoft Internet Explorer 5.0* (or a later version) and *Internet* or *Intranet* connections are required.

We will illustrate the procedure to open an AutoCAD file from the Internet by *Uniform Resource Locator* (URL).

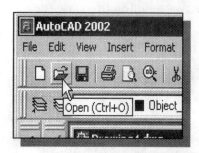

1. Click the **Open** icon in the *Standard* toolbar area as shown.

2. In the *Select File* dialog box, enter http://www.sdcACAD.com/acad2002/Cap-screw.dwg as shown in the figure below.

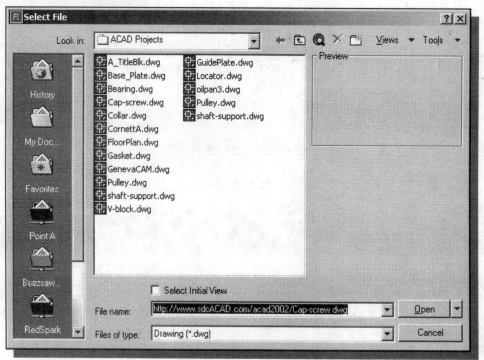

3. Click the **Open** icon and the **Cap-screw** file is downloaded from the www.sdcACAD.com web site to the local computer.

- The URL entered must be of the *Hypertext Transfer Protocol* (http://) and the complete filename must be entered including the filename extension (.dwg or .dwt). Also note that the directory and file names are case sensitive.

Rearrange the Displayed Windows

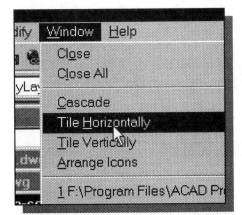

1. In the pull-down menus, select:

   [Window] → [Tile Horizontally]

   ➢ Note that the highlighted window and the graphics cursor indicate the **active window** in the current AutoCAD session. We can switch to any window by clicking inside the desired window.

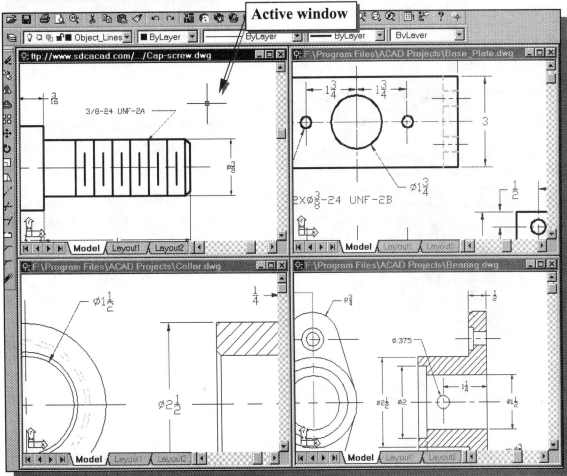

Active window

➢ On your own, adjust the display of each window by left-clicking inside each window and using the ***Zoom Realtime*** command.

Defining a *Block*

1. Set the ***Cap-Screw*** window as the *active window* by left-mouse-clicking inside the window.

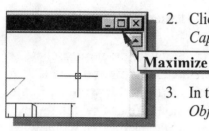

2. Click on the **Maximize** icon at the top-right corner of the *Cap-Screw* window to enlarge the window.

3. In the *Layer Control* box, switch off all layers except the *Object_Lines* and *Center_Lines* layers.

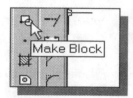

4. Pick the **Make Block** command icon in the *Draw* toolbar. The *Block Definition* dialog box appears on the screen.

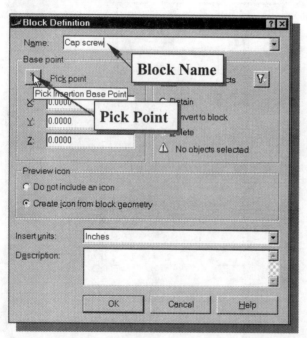

5. In the *Block Definition* dialog box, enter ***Cap screw*** as the block *Name*.

6. Click on the **Pick Point** button to define a reference point of the block.

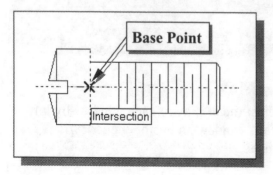

7. Pick the intersection of the centerline and the base of the ***Cap-Screw*** head as the base point.

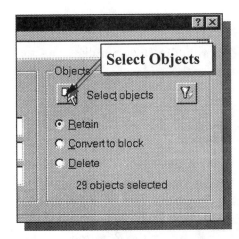

8. Click on the **Select Objects** icon to select the objects to be placed in the block.

9. Select all *object lines* and *centerlines* by using a selection window on the screen.

10. Inside the graphics window, **right-mouse-click** once to accept the selected objects.

- The selected objects will be included in the new block, and several options are available regarding the selected objects after the block is created. We can retain or delete the selected objects or convert them to a block instance.

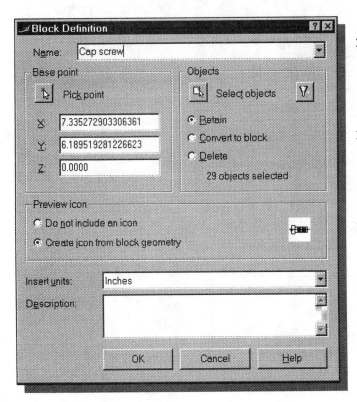

  ➢ **Retain**: Keep the selected objects as regular objects in the drawing after creating the block.

  ➢ **Convert to Block**: Convert the selected objects to a block instance in the drawing after creating the block.

  ➢ **Delete**: Remove the selected objects from the drawing after creating the block.

11. Pick the **Retain** option to keep the objects as regular lines and arcs.

  ➢ Notice in the *Preview icon* section, the *Create icon from block geometry* option displays a small icon of the selected objects.

12. Click the **OK** button to accept the settings and proceed to create the new block.

Inserting a *Block*

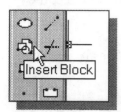

1. Pick the **Insert Block** command icon in the *Draw* toolbar. The *Block Definition* dialog box appears on the screen.

2. In the *Insert* dialog box, notice the block name ***Cap screw*** appears in the block *Name* box. (Note: In this example, we created only one block; AutoCAD allows us to define multiple blocks in the same drawing.)

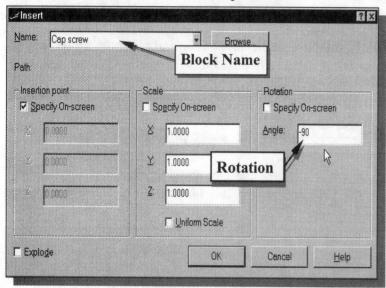

3. In the *Rotation* section, we will enter a **-90** angle to orient the ***Cap screw*** in a vertical direction. Notice that other options are also available. The *Scale* option allows us to adjust the size of the block, and we can also position the block by entering coordinates.

4. Click on the **OK** button to accept the settings and proceed to insert the block into the drawing.

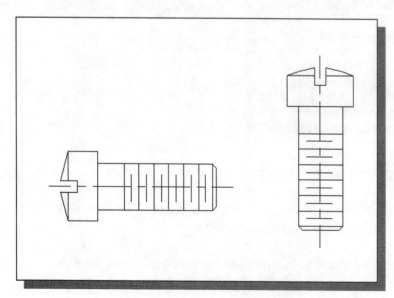

5. Move the cursor toward the right side of the original copy of the cap screw. Left-click to place a copy of the block.

➢ On your own, place additional copies of the block on the screen while experimenting with the *Block Scale* and *Rotation* options.

Starting the *Assembly drawing*

1. Switch back to the four tiled-windows display by left-clicking on the *Maximize* icon near the upper-right corner of the graphics window.

2. Select the **New** icon in the *Standard* toolbar area.

3. In the *AutoCAD 2002 Today* startup dialog box, select the *Template* option as shown in the figure.

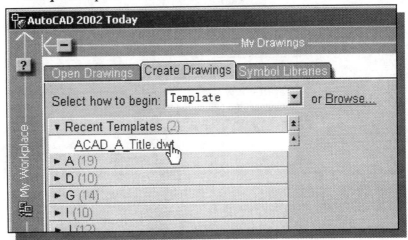

4. Select the *Acad_A_Title* template file from the list of template files. If the file is saved in a separate folder, click on the **Browse** button to locate the file.

5. Click the **OK** button to open the selected template file.

6. On your own, resize the window as shown.

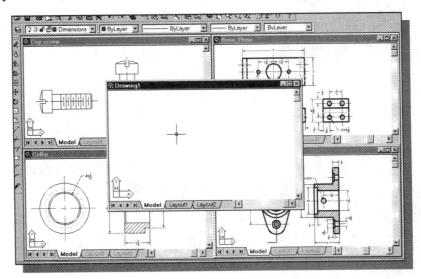

Copying and pasting with the *Windows Clipboard*

1. Set the **Base-Plate** window as the *current window* by left-mouse-clicking inside the window.

2. In the *Layer Control* box, switch off all layers except the *Object_Lines, Hidden_Lines,* and *Center_Lines* layers.

3. Select the **front-view** of the *Base-Plate* by enclosing the front-view using a selection window.

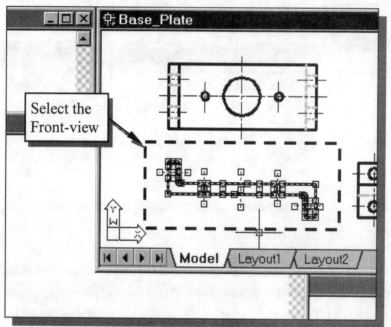

4. Select the **Copy to Clipboard** icon in the *Standard* toolbar area.

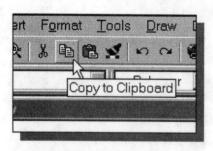

5. Set the **Drawing1** window as the *current window* by a left-mouse-click inside the window.

6. Select the **Paste from Clipboard** icon in the *Standard* toolbar area.

7. Position the front-view of the *Base-Plate* near the bottom of the graphics window as shown.

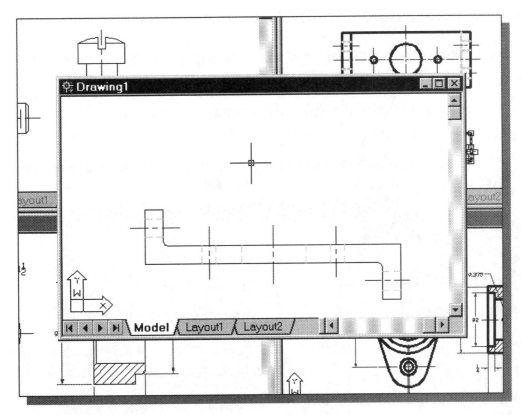

Converting the view into a section view

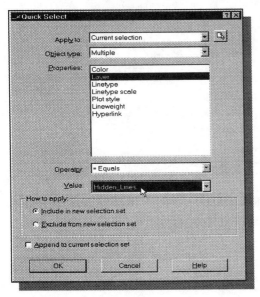

1. Click on the **Maximize** icon at the top-right corner of the *Drawing1* window to enlarge the window.

2. **Pre-select** all the objects in the front-view by using a selection window.

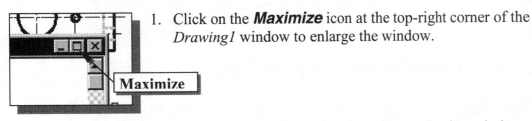

3. Inside the graphics window, **right-mouse-click** to bring up the popup option menu and select the **Quick Select** option.

4. In the *Quick Select* dialog box, select *Layer* from the *Properties* list.

5. Set the *Value* box to *Hidden_Lines*.

6. In the *How to apply* section, confirm the *Include in new selection set* option is selected.

7. Click on the **OK** button to accept the settings.

8. AutoCAD will now **filter out** objects that are not on layer *Hidden_Lines*.

9. In the *Layer Control* box, click on the **Object_Lines** layer name to move the selected objects to the *Object_Lines* layer.

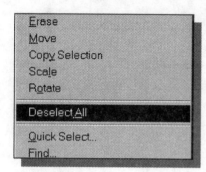

10. Inside the graphics window, **right-mouse-click** and select **Deselect All**.

11. In the *Layer Control* box, set layer **Section_Lines** as the *Current Layer*.

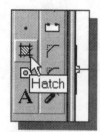

12. Select the **Hatch** icon in the *Draw* toolbar. The *Boundary Hatch* dialog box appears on the screen.

13. On your own, create the hatch-pattern as shown.

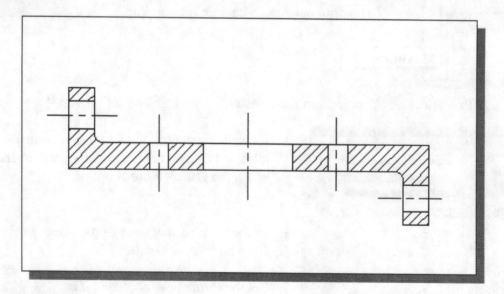

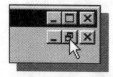

14. Switch back to the tiled-windows display by left-clicking on the *Maximize* icon near the upper-right corner of the graphics window.

Adding the *Bearing* to the assembly drawing

1. Set the *Bearing* window as the *current window* by a left-mouse-click inside the window.

2. In the *Layer Control* box, switch off all layers except the *Object_Lines, Hidden_Lines, Center_Lines*, and *Section_Lines* layers.

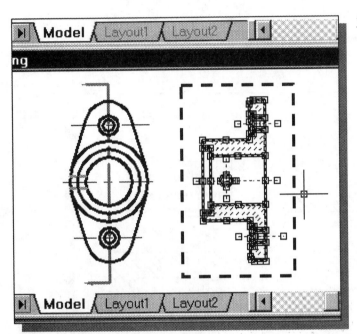

3. Select the **side-view** of the *Base-Plate* by enclosing the side-view using a selection window.

4. Inside the graphics window, **right-mouse-click** and select the **Copy with Base Point** option.

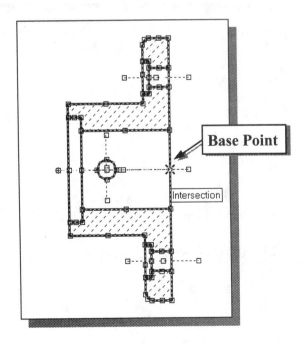

5. Pick the **center-intersection** on the right-vertical line of the side-view as the base point.

6. Set the **Drawing1** window as the *current window* by left-mouse-clicking inside the window.

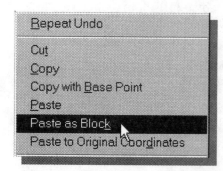

7. Inside the graphics window, **right-mouse-click** and select the **Paste as Block** option.

8. Align the side-view of the bearing to the top center-intersection of the *Base-Plate* as shown.

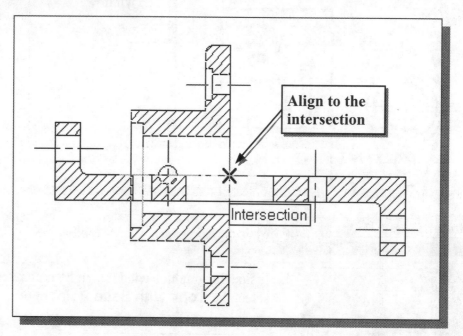

9. Click on the **Rotate** icon in the *Modify* toolbar.

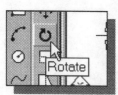

10. Pick the side-view of the *Bearing* we just placed into the assembly drawing. Notice the entire view is treated as a block object.

11. Inside the graphics window, **right-mouse-click** to accept the selection and proceed with the *Rotate* command.

12. Pick the base point as the rotation reference point.

13. Rotate and align the side-view of the *Bearing* to the top of the *Base-Plate*.

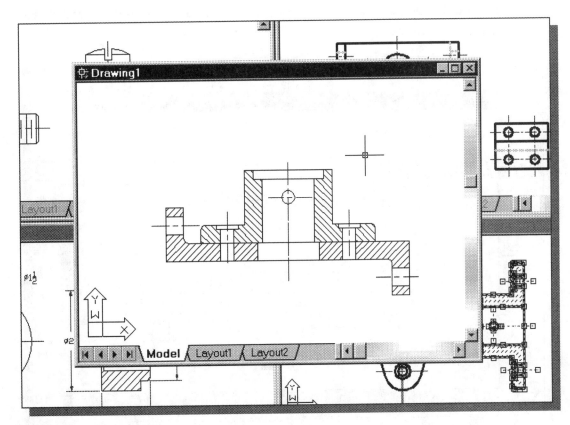

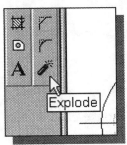

14. Select the **Explode** icon in the *Modify* toolbar.

15. Pick the *Bearing* to break the block into its component objects.

➢ On your own, copy and paste the collar to the top of the bearing.

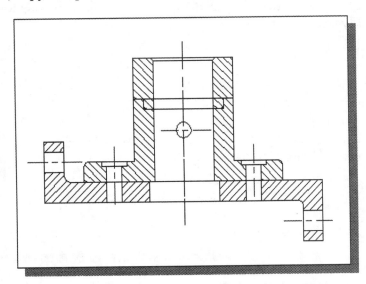

16. Use the **Explode, Trim**, and **Erase** commands and modify the assembly as shown.

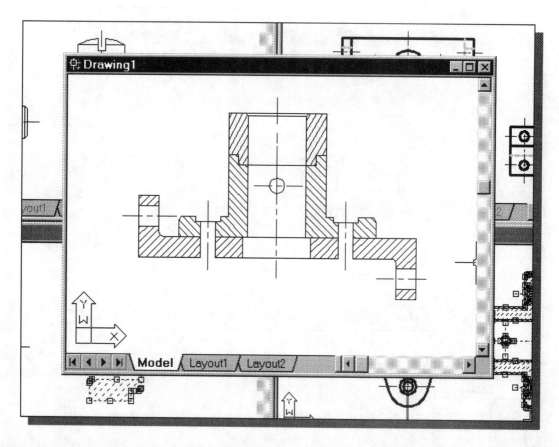

Adding the *Cap-Screws* to the assembly drawing

1. Set the **Cap-Screw** window as the *current window* by a left-mouse-click inside the window.

2. Pre-select the vertical **Cap-Screw**. Since all objects belong to a block we can quickly select the block.

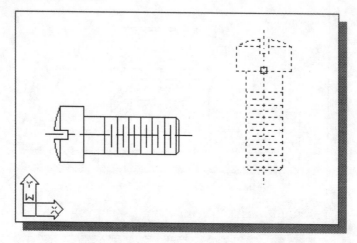

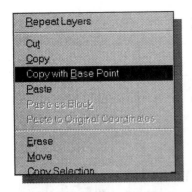

3. Inside the graphics window, **right-mouse-click** and select the **Copy with Base Point** option.

4. Pick the *GRIP* point as the copy base point.

5. Set the *Drawing1* window as the *current window* by left-mouse-clicking inside the window.

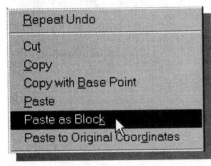

6. Inside the graphics window, **right-mouse-click** and select the **Paste** option.

7. Align the *Cap-Screw* as shown.

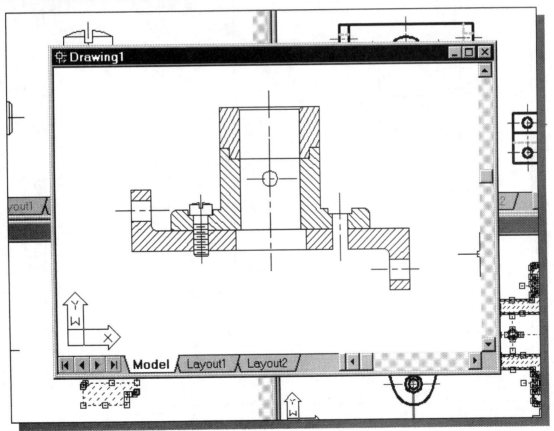

➢ On your own, repeat the steps and place another copy of the *Cap-Screw* in place.

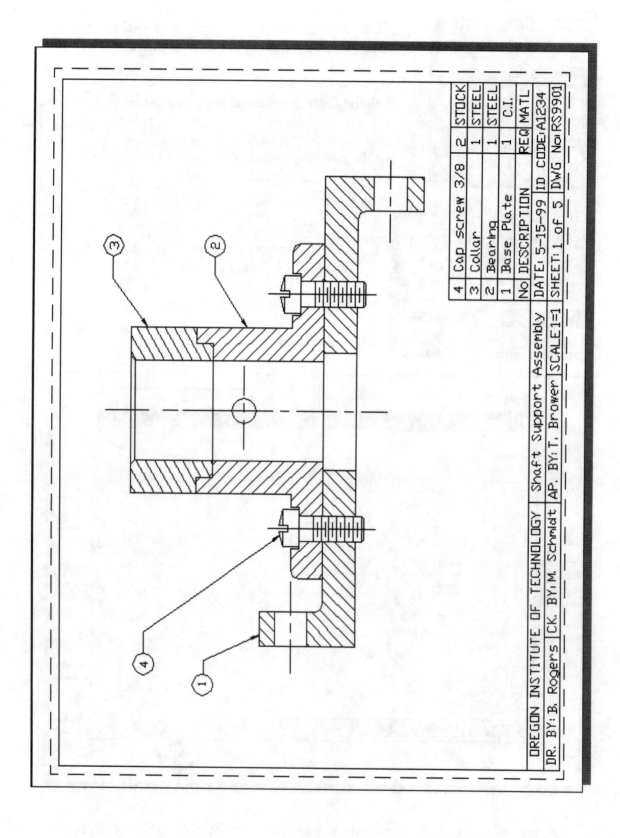

4	Cap screw 3/8	2	STOCK
3	Collar	1	STEEL
2	Bearing	1	STEEL
1	Base Plate	1	C.I.
NO	DESCRIPTION	REQ	MATL

OREGON INSTITUTE OF TECHNOLOGY	Shaft Support Assembly			DATE: 5-15-99	ID CODE: A1234
DR. BY: B. Rogers	CK. BY: M. Schmidt	AP. BY: T. Brower	SCALE 1=1	SHEET: 1 of 5	DWG No: RS9901

Questions:

1. What is an *assembly drawing*? What are the basic differences between an assembly drawing and a detail drawing?

2. What is a *block*? List some the advantages of using blocks in AutoCAD.

3. What are the differences between "*Copying and pasting with the Windows Clipboard*" and "*Copying with GRIPS*"?

4. Which command allows us to separate a block into its component objects?

5. Describe the differences between *PASTE* and *PASTE AS A BLOCK*.

6. Identify the following commands:

   (a)

   (b)

   (c)

   (d)

Exercise:

1. **Wheel Assembly** (Create a set of detail and assembly drawings. All Dimensions are in mm.)

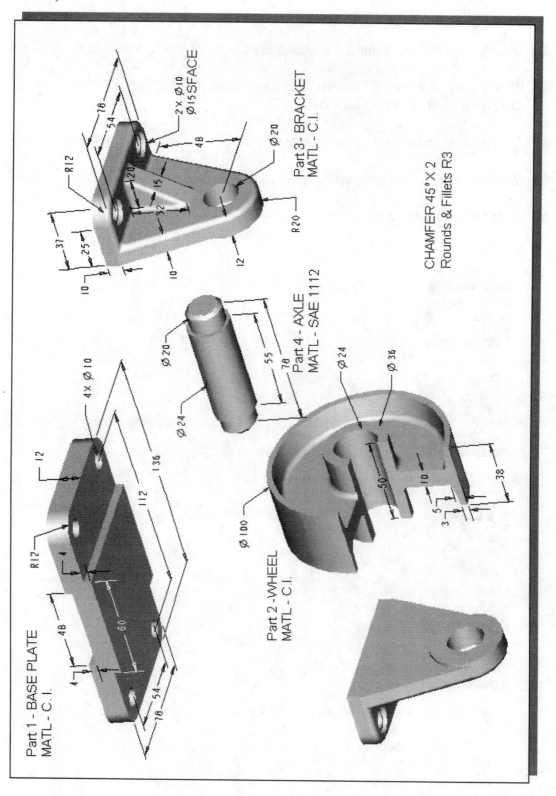

2. **Leveling Assembly** (Create a set of detail and assembly drawings. All Dimensions are in mm.)

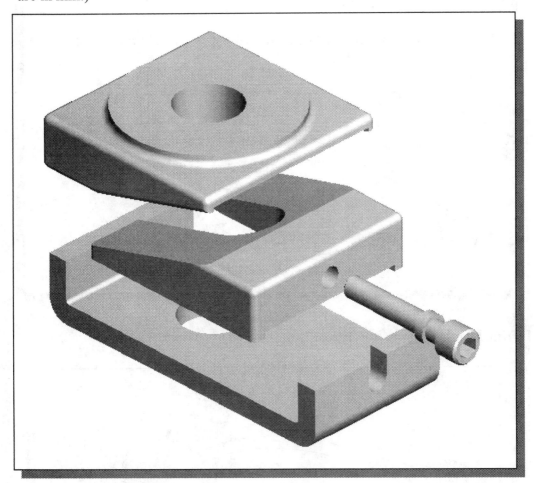

(a) Base Plate

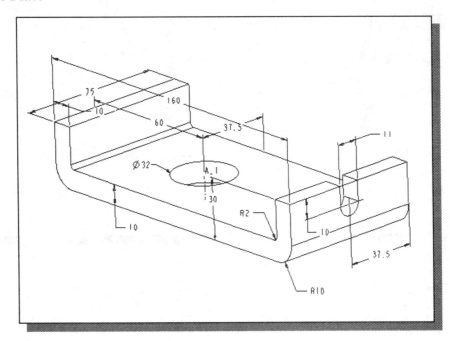

(b) **Sliding Block** (Rounds & Fillets: R3)

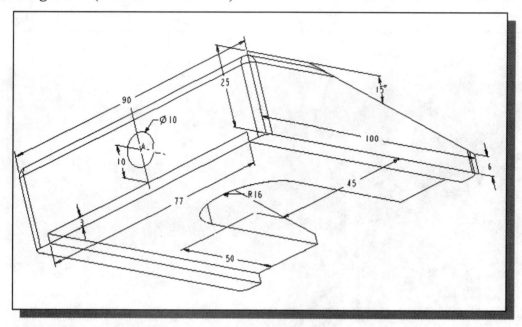

(c) **Lifting Block** (Rounds & Fillets: R3)

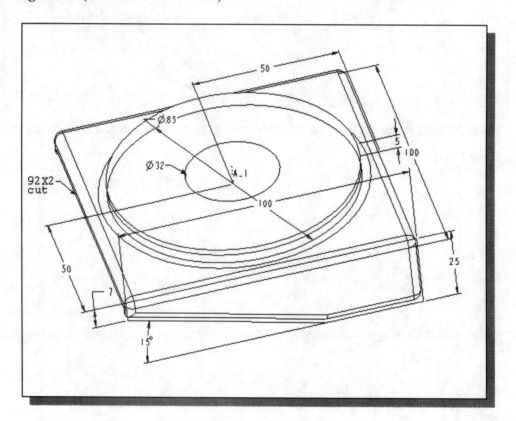

(d) **Adjusting Screw** (M10 X 1.5)

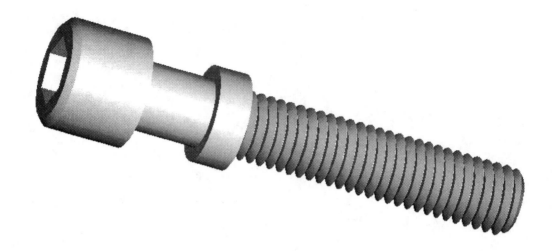

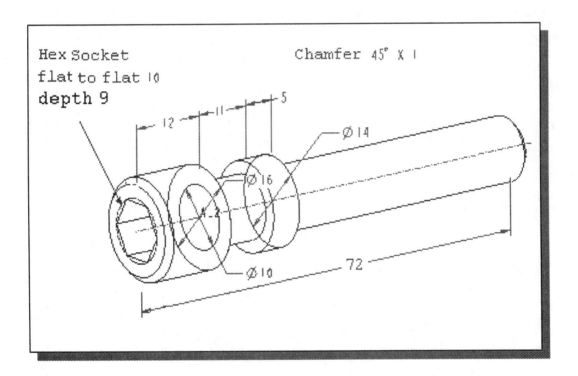

Notes:

INDEX